Dedicated
to my husband John

Acknowledgements

My sincere thanks to:

Morag Hadley for her encouragement and my friends in the Creative Writing Group, Edith, Jean, Terry, Wendy, Betty and Vickie.

Ross Flockhart for kindly writing the Foreword.

Rebecca Quealy, who typed up my original tapes and Kate Blackadder who patiently edited them.

Audrey Limb, Marion Ewing, Walter Cairns and Douglas Smith who all contributed so much in their different ways.

Both Sides of the Fence

Angela Dobbie

The Pentland Press Limited
Edinburgh • Cambridge • Durham • USA

First published in 1996 by
The Pentland Press Ltd.
1 Hutton Close
South Church
Bishop Auckland
Durham

British Library Cataloguing in Publication Data.
A catalogue record for this book is available
from the British Library.

ISBN 1 85821 438 6

Typeset by CBS, Felixstowe, Suffolk
Printed and bound by Antony Rowe Ltd., Chippenham

FOREWORD

This is a story which needed to be told. The story of Angela Dobbie who, as a young nursing Sister, found she was suffering from Disseminated Sclerosis. A story of her gradual realisation of the onset of severe physical disability and of how it affected every aspect of her life. It is a very personal story which tells how it was for her.

Angela Dobbie is descended from a remarkable line of self-made merchants and their families, the Booths in Sydney, Australia, and the Wilkies in Edinburgh. Alexander Wilkie, her father, had sailed to Sydney in 1937 to marry Ida Booth. In the same year they returned to Edinburgh where Angela was born. No thought of the world conflict to come.

I first met Angela in 1940. With her mother and young brother, Alexander, she had arrived in Sydney, where they had been sent to seek refuge with her mother's parents during what became the 1939-45 war. Her father, Alexander, was serving with the Royal Navy in the North Sea. The Booth family lived next door to my family at Wahroonga.

Until she was twenty-four years her life proceeded in the expected manner of a middle-class family in Edinburgh, through school and training to become a nurse. A period full of potential. As a young Ward Sister in London the expected pattern of her life changed dramatically. It unfolded in a distressing and daunting way. Since that time she has become increasingly physically disabled. Occasionally it seemed that all would be well - or reasonably well - but time and again she suffered a further deterioration.

At one level this is a family story of her upbringing in Edinburgh and Australia, her training to be a nurse, her social life, her marriage to John Dobbie and the birth of their daughters Clare and Lisa. Family life is interwoven with the intermittent growth of her disability, periods in hospital and uncertainty about the exact nature of the disease.

At another level it is an honest voice telling how it was - as daughter, wife, mother and friend - facing the fact of her disability. It is a frank story from the inside, through which there shines personal courage as well as penetrating lessons for able-bodied persons and public institutions.

At a third level it is about the society in which she is set and its attitudes to disability, the lack of understanding, often on the part of well-meaning people, and the need for changes in the provision of public services and access for disabled persons.

There is no faking here. No pretentiousness. No pleading for sympathy. She makes fun of herself but does not hide her disappointments and the frustration of her hopes, nor does she hesitate to record the dark periods when she was 'down', 'depressed' or 'devastated'. She does not, however, refer to pain or suffering of which there must have been plenty.

We see her efforts to be for her children an 'ordinary mum' and her constant concern that her disability and dependence on others should inhibit as little as possible the lives of her daughters and husband, John.

The determination and patience it took to speak this book to her tape-recorder over a period of years is a mark of her determination and spiritual courage. These qualities, together with her marriage with John, his understanding, their love for one another, their mutual acceptance of all that marriage in such circumstances can mean, has enabled her to endure and triumph on the other side of the fence.

On reading this book you are bound to discover a very rare kind of person. A vibrant spirit oddly enough set free by the imprisonment of her body.

Ross Flockhart

Edinburgh, August 1996.

CHAPTER ONE

It was hot and everyone else was inside. In front of me was the high white gate. Why were we not allowed to open it? What was in there? Why did I never see anyone go in or come out? Although only three, I was determined to do just that. Looking around to make sure no one could see me, I reached up on tiptoes and slid the latch sideways, pushing my doll in her stroller straight through, leaving the gate wide open. I was thrilled to be in a forbidden place. Sadly, my excitement turned into disappointment. It just seemed to be another paddock, a small one with nothing in it. I couldn't understand what all the fuss had been about. Once again I was feeling bored but a moment later my senses spun round - because coming at me full pelt across the paddock was a large merino ram with its huge curly horns lowered. Dumping my toys I ran as fast as my little legs would take me to the gate. At the same moment my precious doll's stroller was tossed by the horns of the ram up and over the white paling fence. It landed with me in a heap of dust amidst a lot of shouting from Uncle Cecil and Mummy. They couldn't believe it. Why had I opened the gate when they had told me not to? Why was I always naughty?

That was the very first incident that I can remember. The next one was again on the Australian sheep station. My Granny Booth, a tall lady with a wonderful smile, had come up from Sydney. She always wore long dresses with comfortable, ordinary shoes. Somehow she had a grandeur about her. She was not aloof, but warm and loving. We adored her even though she was very strict with us. One of her favourite things to do was to gather us kids, my cousins Hugh and Helen, my brother Alexander and me, out of Mum's and Aunty Linda's way, and especially from Uncle Cecil's beady eyes, and take us for a picnic to a small copse of pine trees a short distance from the homestead - there amongst the pine trees at certain times of the year we could pick delicious mushrooms and boil a billy can of tea over a bonfire. I can still smell those mushrooms and the tea.

My next memories take us, my mother, Alexander and myself, to where we stayed with Granny and Grandpa Booth whose home was in Wahroonga, a suburb on the North Shore line out of Sydney. We really set up as our main base there, I suppose, but it became like our second home. Wahroonga means 'My home in the trees'. Truly it was that – many different kinds of gum trees and tall flowering trees, and my grandfather's beautiful garden which he did all himself and was proud to do so. He was very knowledgeable at it and didn't mind a bit the endless hard work it entailed. I can't really remember the acreage, but I've been there since, and it is quite large. As little ones, it was, of course, huge to us and a wonderful area for playing.

We were there as tiny children, while our father, Alex Wilkie, was on a mine-sweeper made from a converted fishing boat in the North Sea. He'd joined the navy at the beginning of the war, in his early thirties, not easy to be mixed in with young lads who had been recruited at the usual young age. He was there, in that terrible war situation, and we were 12,000 miles away. We children had no understanding of the war. Our mother often spoke of Daddy and took home movies and she'd say, 'We'll send these so that Daddy can watch you growing up.' I didn't have any feelings about my Daddy because I didn't know him; I'd been too little when we had left Scotland to go to Australia. So as we were staying with my grandfather, he became the father figure in my life. There's no doubt about that: all the years of his life my Grandpa Booth meant everything to me. To be honest, even thinking now about him, I find very moving.

Grandpa and Granny Booth's home was called Oakfield, a big rambling house with a large verandah on one side and a curved driveway up to the front door, outside which was a midnight cactus. If you went straight on up the drive, the long verandah was on your right, and on the left opposite that, in the garden, was a large sundial. One of our favourite things was to collect the many, many large snails which frequented the garden. Alexander and I would see if we could make them have races round the top of the sundial.

My grandparents' home had big white steps at the front, and inside on the right, rather a large, posh I'd say, sitting room. We hardly ever went in there. All the way down the left hand side of the house there were bedrooms which led onto this big long verandah. Often when it was hot, the beds would be moved out onto the verandah where we would try to sleep listening to the possums scrabbling around in the guttering and on the roof.

The dining room was a large room which had special significance for me because Granny and Grandpa would sit at either end of their long, polished table. We would be either side of them. After dinner, Granny Booth would sit on when others had moved away, and play patience. I found it fun to budge up next to her and watch her play. It was a great time for a chat, a chance to be alone with her when she wasn't busy in the house or garden. At the far end of the house was the kitchen, very basic, with what they called a breakfast room

Me aged 3 with my stroller on the sheep station

off it. It was quite a sunny room, and that brings me the memory, instantly, of Grandpa and breakfast. Grandpa's breakfast was always the same, an apple. He was a man of routine: always an apple and a cup of coffee. Obviously it suited him since he lived until he was ninety-three.

Right next door there was St John's, a Presbyterian Church. The Reverend and Mrs David Flockhart lived in the manse and, conveniently for us, a small school met in the church hall. Even more conveniently, the fencing between the two properties had a hole in it, just big enough for us little ones to go through. It was like a kindergarten school and, of course, we only went there if we were staying with Granny and Grandpa, so it was very much an on-off start to our education. I don't remember learning about anything, but the one thing I do remember about that little school was the parallel bars in the playground, where we enjoyed hanging upside down pretending to be wombats or koala bears.

My memory then takes me away from my grandparents' home, down to their beach house, Nantucket, at Newport, called after Nantucket Island in America where my grandparents spent their honeymoon. Newport had a wonderful long sandy beach fringed by tall Norfolk pines. Nantucket was just hard board, septic tank, no mod cons, a make-do shower out at the back and a big verandah round three sides of it. Oh, what fun we had down there on the beach and in the water!

One day, my mother had taken Alexander and myself onto the beach as usual. I must have been about five and a half, Alexander four. We were used to the water, and knew not to go too far out because of the huge waves, but our mother, being an Australian, was used to surfing. This particular day, we were playing on the edge when we saw the lifeguards with their red and yellow skull caps rushing down to the water. To our horror, the person they brought out of the water was our mother. It seemed to us – well, we thought she was dead. All we could see, as little people, was her, face down, covered in blood. They carried her up to a suitable place to lay her down, and we didn't know what to do or say. We thought it must be that our mummy was dead. In fact, she had been caught in one of these dangerous waves, a big sand dumper, and completely tumbled over and over; she was choked with sand and her nose was bleeding badly. Our mother soon regained her composure and was quick to be up and pretend that nothing had happened.

One hot night, Christmas Eve, us littlies were in rows like a dormitory, because the extended family used to gather together at Christmas time, and that was all part of the fun too. But as I lay there, I was fed up because everyone else seemed to be asleep and it seemed as if Christmas Day would never come. To my sadness, I saw our mum come from her bedroom very quietly, with two pillow cases, with balloons tied on top, full of pressies for my brother and me, and place one at the end of each of our beds. I did not want her to know that I knew, but I felt so sad, and yet I suppose I had already begun to suspect, as one does as a little child. But then, of course, there was all the fun two hours later, when we all woke up and opened our pressies. We unwrapped every single one, and wrapped them all up again, and then in the morning pretended to see them for the first time.

Back to Sydney. I was about six and a half, school was becoming more important and Grandpa was definitely saying, I want to know if you can write properly. And, of course, to his horror, I couldn't. So it became a habit that he would put up the card table and sit with me for at least an hour every night while I practised copy writing and, under his strict but gentle supervision, I learned to have excellent writing. Another little memory creeps in, my grandmother brushing my long blond hair a hundred times a day. Oh, how boring, I used to think, sitting there, but because I loved her, I let her do it.

CHAPTER TWO

With our Daddy so far away, the war had not really affected Alexander and myself much at all, but of course for our parents it had been awful, with all those years of separation which neither could possibly have anticipated. But we were included in, and felt very much part of, the entire family out there in Australia. Apart from Grandpa and our grandmother there was my mother's brother James, her elder sister Linda, and Jean, Helen and Mary who were younger. Our Aunty Jean's husband Murray Walker, who was in the Australian Air Force, was killed in the war just a short time after their son Freddy was born. Apart from that, we were really removed from what was happening in the rest of the world during the war and it wasn't until we were much older that we came to an understanding of it.

All these years we had been happy surrounded by our warm extended family but soon we were to say goodbye to all of them, and to the only life that we knew – the sunshine, space, running about in lightweight clothes, no shoes – hardly ever wearing shoes. That's why we've all got such broad feet, I guess. I don't remember saying goodbye. But I do remember that Mother worked hard to pack up fruits in Kilner jars, to bring back to Scotland, and different items which were in short supply in Scotland. We boarded the *Andes*, then the fifth largest ship in the world, with hundreds of other women and children who were being repatriated. There were also hundreds of troops returning home, and so we were in our thousands on that enormous ship. That is when, ironically, the war began for my brother Alexander and me, because instead of the freedom of open verandahs, we felt cramped in one cabin which we shared with another family, making seven of us.

There was not a lot of contact with the troops – this was much frowned upon – but we did meet and talk to one or two of them and we found that rather fun. Awesome, we thought, all those uniforms. The heat was horrible, not the happiness we'd experienced in Australia. The ship had to go to Karachi, and wait there for more troops to join the ship. We were delayed there for a whole week, the temperature was well over 100°F, and the humidity equally awful. We were now half way back to the UK. Most of us children had developed measles, so were, hot, itching and scratching. At the same time, many of the troops who were already on board had dysentery and there were also a number of cases of diphtheria, so it was a ship under huge stress. Eventually the long-awaited troops came aboard and we set sail again. What a relief, the movement, a bit of a breeze, a bit of air.

And then, one night out of Karachi, a storm came up suddenly and the ship, huge as it was, started to pitch and roll. Well, before we knew it, and to the most enormous glee of us children, the water, the sea water was coming through the portholes, which were open because of the heat. It was like a shower, whoopee, fantastic! Jump out of bed which is hot and horrible anyway, and let's have a shower and dance about and stamp in the water. Our mothers were demented but, looking back on it, it didn't matter that we were all soaked. It cooled us down, and was a bit of fun which we much needed. But of course, it made a lot of extra work for our mothers. At that time though, my brother and I developed a bit of dysentery along with the measles; we were quite poorly and for that reason we were moved to the sick bay at the stern of the ship. There was an army medical officer in charge who was great, and he told us wonderful stories, ghost stories, army stories, all sorts of things to pass the time. When we were better, though, we were pleased to be back with the other children, but I do remember the daily lifeboat drills.

Our voyage progressed through the Suez Canal, the Mediterranean and the Bay of Biscay and ended at Southampton. Our mother said as we stood peeping through the railings, 'Do you see down there? One of those two men in naval uniforms is your Daddy.' I don't remember feeling anything. I wanted to feel excited, but it is awfully difficult to feel excited about someone you don't know. However, we came off the ship and our Daddy was a warm and gentle person, full of fun, and it wasn't difficult at all to get to know him. You can imagine the overjoyed excitement of our parents to be together again, and for all four of us to be together. So then, from the ship, we had a long train journey, which I don't remember. But the arrival in Scotland, I will never forget. Three o'clock in the morning, Waverley Station, Edinburgh. Not the best of times to arrive anywhere. We didn't have enough warm clothes on.

Suddenly, after having been so hot, we were freezing. Then there was a taxi, of course, far too much luggage. I don't remember, but I think there were others to help us. The excitement of our parents was mixed in with the bewilderment of my brother and myself. We were driven to Granny Wilkie's home, 14 Ravelston Park.

Since it was early in the morning our grandmother was not awake. It was Aunt Connie who welcomed us. She showed Alexander and me up to the third floor of what seemed an enormous, cold house. She said, 'I want you both to get undressed and into your beds. Get some sleep and we will talk about everything in the morning.' I was dying to get my shoes off, so that was the first thing to do – big mistake, chilly linoleum on the floor. Then as I jumped into bed and pulled the covers up, I thought, Oh my goodness whatever is that? Something else that is freezing, it's like a stone, and it's in my bed. And in my fury I kicked the dashed thing out. I heard this crash and when I peered over the side of the bed, there was cracked stoneware and water all over the floor. And I'm thinking, Oh Angela, what have you done now? In this strange place, everyone will be furious. I pulled the bedcovers up and went straight to sleep.

The following morning I shall not ever forget. We met Daddy's mother, Granny Wilkie, for the first time: a short roundish lady, very smart but awesome, we thought. She seemed warm and loving enough, but we felt very shy of her that first morning. Aunt Connie seemed equally formidable. Into the dining room – a large room with polished antique furniture. As we sat down at the table these bowls were placed in front of us. I looked down, and thought, Whatever can that be? It all looked very glue-like to me, and it had the odd lump in it. I took a spoonful, and thought, Oh no. It was sort of in my mouth and it hadn't gone down, whatever was this? Granny Wilkie's beady eyes were upon us, and she said, 'Now, you two, this is porridge, we have it every morning, and you'll eat it up. If you don't eat it up now, it will go in the sideboard cupboard and you can have it for lunch.' Well, the very thought of it being kept for hours to be absolutely stone cold and brought out again! I thought, No, better get it over with, eat it up now. So we did just that, but not without much misery. So quite honestly, those first twenty-four hours here, in our Scottish grandmother's home, were hard, unhappy and cold. All we longed to do, Alexander and I, was to go right back to Australia.

CHAPTER THREE

Daddy had a certain amount of leave and took us up to Aberdeen, where we met the Walkers, the Burnetts and Aunty Curls and Michael Bruce, all families who had looked after our father when he was on leave. Alexander and I had a marvellous time being shown all round our Daddy's ship, the *Ligny*. We couldn't believe how cramped it all was compared to the space we'd had in the last five years. Sadly for me, the news came through that they could get an interview for me at the school right opposite our Granny Wilkie's home. It was called St George's School for Girls. So along we went and, to my disappointment, but to our parents' delight, the school accepted me, and said that I could start immediately.

Lucky Alexander, the Edinburgh Academy where they were hoping that he would be able to go didn't have a place then for him. So he was able to return north to Aberdeen. That left me in Edinburgh, knowing that I would have to stay with my Granny Wilkie, my maiden Aunt Connie and Aunt Evie. My initial experiences at school were really as awful as I'd dreaded. Firstly, I was still quite sun-tanned so I looked different. I had an Australian accent and that was wrong, and thirdly, of course, I didn't know anybody. Nearly everyone else had been there since they were five, so they'd made special friends. I was very lonely and felt like a fish out of water. In the playground – now, there's a lonely place when you don't know anybody and you don't feel that anyone likes you or that anyone wants to talk to you. One day the other girls tied me to a tree.

The teachers, I know, were doing their best and I didn't feel that they were being hard on me, except in terms of my writing. 'Well, Angela, we don't have writing with loops here at St George's. You'll have to cut out the loops.' To my astonishment, they insisted on me completely changing my writing. What a mistake that was, but in those days, it was thought the right thing to do, to make everyone conform. So what had been very good copy writing became a distinct mess, lacking in character.

My Granny Wilkie and Aunt Connie were doing their very best to make me feel more at home. They had given me a banana for my breaktime one day, and I thought, a banana, well, that's fine, thank you very much. But of course, a banana to Angela Wilkie, who'd been living in Australia, wasn't anything special. I put it in my schoolbag. At breaktime, not knowing at all what was about to happen, I took my banana out of the schoolbag. The entire class seemed to descend on me like a swarm of bees. I thought, What is it? They were all screaming and shouting, 'A banana, a banana!' I asked if they would like it? Then they were all screaming, 'Yes, yes!' and squabbling over it, by which time it had been thrown about the classroom. I didn't understand it, but of course they had not had the fruit we'd been lucky enough to enjoy, and a banana was something special. I didn't care but I thought, well, there was a little hope, even a funny little hope, that if they had my banana they might think better of me. It's amazing how hopeful you can be in such a bad situation.

Back at 14 Ravelston Park, with Mummy, Daddy and Alexander still in Aberdeen, it was approaching my eighth birthday and I thought, imagine my birthday in this place where I'm so unhappy. But there was a surprise, quite a big one I thought: a bicycle for my birthday. I was thrilled. It was my first real happy feeling since coming back to Edinburgh. But soon we all moved into our own home which they had bought before the war, 12 Lennel Avenue, and there it was, with the name of it, Wahroonga. That made me feel better already.

Quite soon after the war, my parents had their third child, Mary, who had the most gorgeous golden hair. What a lovely little girl, and absolutely the centre of attention because she was the only little one of that age around.

The first nice thing that happened at school was starting to know a girl called Audrey, who is my best friend to this day. I did gradually make other friends at school: Joy, Helen, Pixie, Aitchie and Jackie. So I built a circle of friends, but when it came to playing at home, it was much more boy orientated. There was Alexander and a friend down the road, Norman Lessels, and the three of us got on very well, so we became a little gang.

I had another sister, Sue, born two years after Mary. I remember going to the nursing home in Randolph Crescent where she was born. All I could see was a mop of black hair and a darling little face, and being told that this was my new little sister. By this time I was eleven, and more capable and able to be helpful to our mother. I really enjoyed that. I suppose my mother needed the help, which was why she taught me lots of things. But there was another side to it. I think, being an Australian, she had different attitudes towards children. She was more forward in her thinking and never worried about what others thought.

There was a sadness running through these years in that our Daddy didn't always seem to be so well. Nobody ever said why. It was more that he seemed

Alexander and I, aged 7 and 8, outside Granny Wilkie's house in Edinburgh

worried a lot, not that he was physically unwell. But in those days people did not explain anything to children. Mother would sometimes say that he had to go for a whole weekend to see a special doctor. She never said what kind of doctor, or what it was about, and Daddy would never explain. We didn't somehow like to ask; we felt it wouldn't be right. Also at this time, Susan was about nine months old and had developed that dreaded infantile eczema. That put such stress on our parents and that wee soul, as they plastered her in cream after cream and tried every different type of treatment, splinting her arms to stop her scratching. The whole thing was a nightmare, until eventually she was taken into the Royal Infirmary where she was seen by a completely different skin specialist. An extraordinary thing, but true: she was not allowed visitors at all. In those days it was thought that visits, even from parents, would upset the child. How completely reversed is the thinking nowadays. I'm glad that it is, because Susan was there for at least nine weeks. I remember that the day she came home she could sit up, and Mummy put her on the sitting room floor. It was just ourselves, Mum, Dad, myself, Alexander and Mary. I suppose we were in a sort of family circle and Susan was in the middle, those vacant eyes staring at each one of us in turn, not knowing any of us, not even one of us.

During the early years back in Edinburgh, we made lots of new friends, some through school, but some were the children of long-standing friends of our parents. Amongst these were several families in particular with whom we spent holidays, often at North Berwick: the Lamberts, the Harpers, the Gibbs and the Parkers, who are still special today. Alexander and I first learned to play golf on the children's course in North Berwick and then we became members of Murrayfield Golf Club, Edinburgh. We played golf all the time and it gave us hours of fun.

When I was twelve, Mum and Dad decided to move house and bought a large three-storeyed house in Ravelston Park, almost opposite Granny Wilkie, in fact backing right onto the big playing fields of St George's School. It was the time of the Queen's Coronation, and also when we had television for the first time. On the day of the Coronation, in London it was pouring with rain. In Edinburgh, however, the sun was shining, and to be honest, although I adore the Queen and I think she stands for everything that is fine, I have to admit I became quickly bored with all the pageantry. I thought, what a waste sitting inside, how stuffy it is, I'm fed up with this. I remember rushing out into the garden – we had a much bigger garden now – and thinking I'd much prefer to be out in the sunshine than sitting watching a small black and white box.

Granny Wilkie died six months after we had moved into Ravelston Park and, ironically, she left her house to our father, the eldest of the family. After Granny Wilkie died, I realised, sadly, that I had hardly known her. The house was sold and Aunty Connie moved into 13 Chester Street. That was when I really got to know her properly. She asked me to come and stay for a night, and as she worked in the family business, I thought I could make myself useful and offered to make the dinner. I had done simple meals at home and was quite used to that sort of thing. Aunt Connie was delighted by my suggestion. Unfortunately, as is often the way when you are trying hard, I had a disaster with the mince. I wasn't used to electricity; we always cooked on gas at home. Leaving the mince to simmer, I thought I would set the table, arrange some flowers, and make everything tidy. To my horror, I could smell burning, and as I opened the kitchen door this cloud of smoke met me. Well, I'd not only burnt the mince, the dinner, but also the saucepan, and blackened the walls of Aunt Connie's immaculate flat. So when she came up the stairs expecting to find dinner ready, she was met by a smell of burning and a blackened kitchen. I was quite frightened of what she might say to me, but she was sweet and not angry at all, and we laughed about it and had something else for dinner. That was when I got to know her well, to love her and to find out that she was in fact a fun person with a great sense of humour.

Her youngest sister, Irene, was a very smart lady, married to Daddy's best friend, Cecil Stevenson. We saw them quite a lot in their beautiful house down at Dunbar. To complete a simple picture of the Wilkie family, I must tell you about Grandpa Wilkie who died in 1933. In 1898 he started the Company of Alexander Wilkie Ltd, as a small furrier and tailoring business, in Shandwick Place, Edinburgh. From that grew the large company which it is nowadays, with eight branches. People rarely spoke of Grandpa Wilkie, except to mention his love of walking, and a book that he wrote, *The Call of the Hills*. Granny Wilkie, together with Aunty Connie and Aunty Evie, ran the business during the war, but my father's other sister, Winnie, was away in Kenya and I learned to know and love her later. Another member of the family whom I never met was a younger son, Harry, who had sadly died of anthrax at eighteen while working on a sheep station.

A strange thread about Australia which started long before I was born. Many such threads run through my life, which you will learn about later.

In no time at all, people were beginning to ask me what I was going to do when I left school. For as long as I could remember, I had been bandaging dolls and playing at hospitals and had a clear idea in my mind that I wished to be a nurse. My great friend Audrey shared this ambition and we had this idea that we ought to find out as much as possible about where we should do our training. Everyone was saying that we should go to the Royal Infirmary here in Edinburgh, but we suddenly realised that we didn't know anything much about it. We went along to a career talk on nursing, at the end of which we spoke to the lecturer. What did she think, what was her opinion of nursing here in Edinburgh? Or what about going to London? 'Oh,' she said, 'there's no difficulty in answering that, you must think in terms of a London training. The Royal Infirmary is excellent, but you've lived your lives here up to now, or most of them, and I urge you both to apply to the London teaching hospitals. They are very difficult to get into.'

Already we were feeling more than a little daunted. 'Oh, don't be disheartened,' she said, 'the great thing is to put your name down and to get an interview.'

It all suddenly sounded rather serious, but we were keen and it helped us such a lot to have her opinion, because quite honestly, when we went home to our respective families and announced what we were going to do, the shock was enormous from everybody around us. There was no encouragement at all. My family did not want me to do nursing and felt I should go into the business or think of something else. It was extraordinary, really: we were quite hurt in a way that there we were, with a clear idea of what we'd like to do, but nobody wanted us to do it.

However, I sent away for the brochures, and they all came back and we read through them. There was The Middlesex, St Thomas's, Bart's, Guy's and St Mary's. We applied to The Middlesex and were both granted interviews at the age of sixteen. Well, we went to London, Audrey and I, with our respective mothers, despite all their opposition to our plans. When we got there it seemed so exciting. Already we wanted all the more to be accepted. The Matron, Miss Marriott, was extremely businesslike and said to us,

'You seem to be sensible and set on this idea, but it's a long time before you can come. You'll have to wait until you are nearly nineteen.' That seemed like forever away, but we had been warned about that in the brochure.

Then she said, 'Of course, we can take only one in ten of the people who apply. Medicals are very strict, so I can't really say how you might do. I mean, on paper, you seem to be taking the right exams, but it will depend on those results, your medical and the numbers applying. I urge you, if we do offer you a place here, I want you, after leaving school, to go away somewhere completely different. Do anything you like, but don't do anything to do with nursing. Don't for goodness sake go to a pre-nursing school. Don't have anyone persuade you to do that. Go away and grow up. The best nurses start having grown up a bit before they come to the nursing school.'

CHAPTER FOUR

Two weeks later, we heard that we had both been accepted at The Middlesex Hospital in Mortimer Street, which made me work even harder and start to wonder what I would do between school and going to London. My parents amazed me by suggesting that I should have a year out in Australia. These days a year out is quite a common thing to do, but then it certainly wasn't. I thought it sounded fantastic. The plan was, providing I got my exams, that I could go out to Australia, come back the following summer and, all being well, start at The Middlesex that August.

The exams came and went. It was always hot. Scotland is not known for its hot weather, but somehow, in my experience, it was always hot when we were doing exams. And, of course, that ghastly wait for the results. We were away on a family holiday at Cruden Bay, where there was golf and tennis and wonderful beaches. I remember walking round the garden of the hotel, holding the brown envelope addressed in my own handwriting. I remember Daddy coming out of the hotel looking for me. 'Well?' he said.

I could hardly speak. 'I haven't opened it, I can't bear to look.'

'Would you like me to do it?'

'Oh no, no, I'd rather do it myself.'

I couldn't believe it, I'd managed to get them all. This meant so much, it meant that all the plans we had made in the hope that I would manage to do it could now take place. I don't remember feeling scared about going away. My experience of Australia up to the age of eight, which I have told you about, had brought me close to all the family over there, so I did not feel that they would be strangers.

My mother knew a lady who was married to a senior person in the Australian Navy. She and her little girl were going out to Australia by ship, and my parents arranged for me to travel with them. That eased my parents' minds because, after all, it wasn't quite the thing, to be swanning across the world, aged seventeen and a half.

After six happy weeks on board the SS *Strathnaver*, and so many new experiences, my excitement was mounting. We were arriving in Sydney the next day. Everything was packed and after our last night of dancing to Glenn Miller's music I went to bed quite early, because the ship was docking at 6 a.m. Well, up we got and cold indeed it was. August in Sydney was cold, just like Mother had said, so I had my tweed suit on that she had insisted on packing, and wasn't I glad of that? Yes, I admit I was. We were all hanging over the rails of the ship, peering down to see if there was anyone we might know. Suddenly, I picked out my grandfather. Oh, wonderful, and beside him, Aunty Jean, and they were waving furiously at me and shouting, 'Angela, welcome to Australia!' I'd arrived – I couldn't believe it. It was fantastic.

At long last the gangways were lowered and we were allowed off. Firstly to the Customs Hall, where I had to identify and claim my luggage – W for Wilkie, at the far end of the Hall, of course.

However, Grandpa and Aunty Jean gathered me and all my luggage together. We drove through the city, across the Sydney Harbour Bridge, up the North Shore Line. I always think of it as the garden route, because all the homes up there have such beautiful gardens. In those days, it wasn't the busy highway that it is now.

I had so much to ask them. Where was I going to stay? Aunty Jean, being practical, said, 'We've been thinking, Angela, we think you ought to make your base with me in Warrawee.'

I said, 'But what about Granny and Grandpa?'

'Well,' she said, 'of course you can stay with them often and stay with me sometimes. I think we will go and say hello to Granny now, before we go back to my house.'

The joy of arriving at Oakfield: there was Granny, standing, tall, her white hair swept up and as always a beautiful smile on her face, her long navy and white dress almost down to her ankles. Standing on the top steps there with their fabulous garden in front. It was like coming home. I felt completely happy.

After an emotional time with Granny and Grandpa, Aunty Jean said that it was time to go. She drove me to her home, 9 Pibrac Avenue, Warrawee, a spacious, elegant house with another wonderful garden. Aunty Jean showed me upstairs to what I thought was a marvellous big bedroom.

'This can be for you, Angela, and you can count it as yours for as long as you are here in Australia. Make this your base, feel that you are free to come and go.'

Aunty Jean, as I mentioned before, had become a widow during the war, and she'd brought up her daughter Trish and her son Freddy on her own. She never allowed her sadness to cut her off from happiness and fun; she was outgoing and a very sensitive person. Many would say formidable, but because

Granny and Grandpa Booth on their Golden Wedding anniversary

of her kindness and generosity, she shared everything she had with many different people and in such a beautiful way that they did not feel beholden. Even on my first day I was wondering if I would meet young people my own age. Aunty Jean seemed to sense this and said,

'Angela, you have lots of cousins and in particular Jim and Don, the twins, who are just a year older than you.'

Sadly, their father James, my mother's only brother, had died suddenly in his early forties. We'd seen Uncle James over in Scotland quite a lot because he used to travel for the wool company which was one of my Grandpa's businesses. So, although I had seen their father recently, I did not know Jim and Don at all. As we were speaking, I sensed that Aunty Jean wanted to reassure me and she said,

'You will meet lots of young people at different places and at different times, but right now you need a good night's sleep and we will see what tomorrow brings.'

The following day brought wonderful family and friends who called at different times to welcome me to Australia, to love me and to ask what they could do to give me a happy time. There was not only my mother's family but also a wonderful sister of my father who happened to live near my grandparents. Aunty Evie had lived in Australia since she married an air force pilot after the war. I was overwhelmed by all the offers of hospitality. 'I think you will need a diary,' Aunty Jean was saying from the back of the room.

I wasn't worried about meeting people older than myself. I was shy about meeting my own age group. I felt that I wouldn't be up to their standard at sport, although I did play a reasonable game of tennis and was a strong swimmer. And, of course, not knowing their friends either, I would find that difficult too. But somehow, the way things turned out, I didn't meet them all at once. I met them gradually. Both Aunty Evie and Aunty Jean had parties for me.

Aunty Evie's party was for my eighteenth birthday. She persuaded me to let her dye my white cotton dress. I was horrified but trusted her experience from the family fashion business in Edinburgh. She dyed it beautifully, and the colour – wow, it was shocking pink – which looked fantastic and showed off the tan I had acquired on board ship. It just gave me that little edge of confidence, since everyone else was pale at the end of the Australian winter! So gradually I eased into the teenage scene and there's no doubt about it, the major factor in this was meeting my twin cousins, Jim and Don Booth. Tremendous fun, good looking guys, totally different from each other despite being twins. They and their girlfriends Marg and Helen took me under their wing.

One night Jim invited me to go into the city to have dinner. I wondered if Marg was coming too but, no, he said she wasn't. He said, 'I'm going to take you to have oysters, the best oysters in the whole world.' I thought, oysters, oh no, but Jim said that I would adore them, he knew I would. When we arrived at this posh hotel, I thought, this is going to cost a fortune, I hope I'm going to like them. Jim ordered a dozen for each of us. Well, along came the oysters, open of course, on a large plate of crushed ice with lemon on top, and a special tomato sauce in a beautiful little dish, and with brown bread and butter to go with it. I looked down at the oysters and Jim said, 'Aren't you going to start?' He knew perfectly well that I had not a clue what to do with them, so he relented and showed me what to do. I was sitting there transfixed, thinking, I'll probably choke. I put on the lemon juice and a little touch of tomato sauce, loosened the oyster from its shell, picked it up and poured it down my throat. I didn't choke but I certainly didn't like it. Inwardly I'm thinking, awful, eleven more to go! Jim's face in front of me - great, aren't they? I didn't know what to say except I had to admit to Jim that I didn't like them much.

'Oh well,' he said, 'by the time you've had one or two, I know you will.'

I did try several more because I didn't want to be a spoil-sport, but in the end the only way I could get them down was to pile on the tomato sauce and consumed with them an entire plate of brown bread and butter. An expensive night out but not a happy one for me.

However, knowing Jim and Don gave me an entry to all the young people with whom I enjoyed tennis, swimming, surfing and barbecues.

CHAPTER FIVE

The first family I went to stay with outside Sydney was Aunty Helen and Uncle Peter Fitzsimons; that's Mum's second youngest sister, who had four children, David, Andrew, Martin and Cathy. Everyone adored Aunty Helen. She was a person who never said an unkind word about anyone.

When I arrived at their fruit farm fifty kilometres outside Sydney it was nearly dark so I did not have much time to get my bearings. I was quite tired, and glad they go to bed early in the country, so we hadn't time for much of a chat. I felt very new to the country, not knowing anything about it, but excited, wondering what it would be like.

When I woke up I could hear voices at the far end of the narrow hall, so I had a quick wash and made my way along to the kitchen. Everyone was just finishing breakfast and about to get up from the table.

I said, 'Oh dear, I'm late.'

'Oh no, it's fine,' said Aunty Helen. She is such a relaxed lady.

The three boys left for school. Uncle Peter said he was off down to the dam and he'd see us later, so that left Aunty Helen, myself and little Cathy, aged two. I remember Aunty Helen saying something about the Aga – she thought it had gone out, and as Uncle Peter left, he called back over his shoulder, 'It's all right, I think I've got it going again, I did the usual on it.' I didn't think anything of that because I didn't know what they were talking about.

After breakfast, I left the table and went along the central hall of this long, rambling country house of theirs. There were bedrooms down the right hand side with verandahs off them; there were bathrooms and cupboards on the left and a smaller room where I was at the end of the hall. I was making my bed quickly and wondering what the day would bring, when suddenly I heard the most chilling screams and as I ran along the hall I could see my aunt coming towards me. We met in the middle of their home, right in the middle of the hall there.

Her tee-shirt was on fire, her hair was on fire. I could see the skin, thin sheets of it coming off her neck and her face. I couldn't believe it, my eyes couldn't comprehend it. My brain was saying, smother the flames, and there on my right was their bathroom. Bath towels, I thought, smother gently, smother the flames. Meanwhile Cathy was standing behind my aunt, hanging onto the end of her skirt and crying in fear and fright. I helped my aunt to lie on their bed. It all seemed to take only a few moments but the horror was only beginning. There she lay before me, almost unconscious. 'Angela,' she said, 'Angela, soda bic, soda bic.' I thought, soda bic, sodium bicarbonate. Thank goodness my mother brought us up to know what was in the kitchen.

I rushed to the kitchen, looked along the shelves, everything higgledy-piggledy. However, I found the soda bic, and put the whole lot in the sink. I filled it up with cold water and went back to my aunt. 'The sheets, the sheets,' she said, another pause and then, 'The cupboard by the bathroom,' and then she would drift off again. All this time the wee one was crying, holding on to me or trying to, but I just had to attend to Aunty Helen first. I pulled the cupboard doors open, took a couple of big sheets, rushed to the kitchen sink, shook the sheets apart a bit and soaked them in the soda bic water. No idea what the solution strength was, but it was the best I could do. Then I took the wet sheets and laid them over my aunt. At that moment I thought of my strong desire to be a nurse. But I hadn't had the training yet; I needed it now. However, I had got the sheets over her, and as she lay there I sensed they soothed her, and she seemed to drift off a little, maybe into unconsciousness. That gave me a moment to turn to Cathy and give her a hug while I thought what to do next.

Of course, to get Uncle Peter, but where was he? My mind flew back to breakfast, which now seemed hours ago. He had said he was going to the dam, where was that? I couldn't even remember. In fact, no one had said where it was, and even if they had it wouldn't have meant anything to me. The telephone, of course, the telephone, how stupid. I looked at it. It wasn't like any kind of telephone I'd ever seen. On the wall it was, with something you had to wind up. Again a complete block in that because I was new to the country I didn't know how to work it. There was no way I could expect my aunt to tell me, or little Cathy. I knew I urgently needed help for my aunt. I stood there in the kitchen, holding Cathy tight, and as I looked out of the window, forcing my mind to think of something, I saw my uncle's truck sitting out there. How strange, I thought, why hadn't he taken it to the dam? Maybe the dam wasn't far. But it was hopeless, I couldn't drive and even if I could, I would quickly have become lost. And then I managed to think of something and it was truly wonderful. The horn in the truck! I dashed out and sat there with Cathy on my lap and pressed the horn. I decided it was no good pressing it once, he would think it was Cathy playing, so then I thought I must do something in a repeated fashion – wish I'd been a Girl Guide – so that if Uncle

Peter could hear he would somehow receive the message that we needed help. So I pressed on the horn, one, two, three, then I would pause, and I did this over and over again. In between I would pop into the house to see Aunty Helen who was just conscious and in so much pain, and I felt so helpless.

It seemed forever, but I don't think it was more than about five minutes before Uncle Peter appeared.

'Is there anything wrong?' he asked.

'Oh, Uncle Peter, yes, it's Aunty Helen, there's been a terrible accident. I don't know what happened, but there's been a fire and Aunty Helen is very poorly.'

As he swept through the bungalow and rushed into their room, I was trying to save him from seeing her without any warning, seeing her lying there with the sheets over her face. I told him she was not unconscious, but very badly burned. He was amazing. He rushed to the phone, dialled the Emergency Services and returned to their room saying, 'Well, I don't believe it.'

I said, 'What is it, aren't they sending an ambulance?'

'No,' he said, shaking his head. 'They haven't got one just now. We have got to get Helen into the back of the car.'

I knew little about burns but I did have enough common sense to realise that in an ordinary car the extra damage would be too awful.

'There's nothing else for it,' Peter said, 'I'll bring the car round from the shed.'

The pain, we had nothing to give my aunt for the pain. It seemed quite wrong but there was nothing else we could do. We got her gently into the back of the car, and I sat in front with Cathy. We had to go slowly, slowly for my Aunt Helen and yet as quickly as we could, to Gosford, about fifteen miles away.

What a long way it was, round many hairpin bends, going down a very steep hill most of the way. The nightmare continued. But when we arrived at the hospital, my aunt had become unconscious; at least she couldn't feel the pain. There was nothing more Uncle Peter and I could do and the hospital advised us to go home.

I returned with Uncle Peter to their house. The hours had flashed by and the boys were home from school. How glad I was that my mother had taught me how to cook basic food, because I was suddenly pitched in to be mum to these children, needing to look after them, cook meals for them and most of all to love them.

That night Uncle Peter explained how they were in the habit of relighting the Aga with methylated spirit in a tin. At a later date Aunty Helen told us how she had thought the meths flame was out and had poured more spirit on, resulting in the flames leaping up in her face.

Aunty Helen had to stay in hospital for many months, cushioned in a sling, while the burns healed. Then later she had to have a number of painful skin grafts.

A terrible day I shall never forget.

CHAPTER SIX

I acted as mum for the Fitzsimons family for a week and much enjoyed the country life, then I returned to my base at Aunty Jean's.

At Christmas I was desperately homesick but Hogmanay at Bilgola Surf Club where we had a barbecue and dancing on the beach was the best New Year I can remember.

One day Aunty Jean suggested that I might want to go up to Aunt Linda and Uncle Cecil's sheep station. I thought, wonderful. I couldn't wait to go back up there after fourteen years. Aunty Linda came to pick me up, a round trip for her of fourteen hundred miles. My cousins Hugh and Helen were at boarding school in Sydney but the three youngest ones were at home with a governess, Morrie.

My first impressions of Ercildoune were of the redness of the dirt, the light and the flatness of those 15,000 acres. I have to admit I was still scared of Uncle Cecil. He asked me on my second day there if I would like to ride out with him and the jackaroos. I didn't like to say that I wasn't very keen on horses, in fact I was terrified of them, but I agreed to go.

The next morning Uncle Cecil brought two horses round to the door and before I knew it he had me up on one of them. Suddenly he said, 'I have to nip back into the house for something.' So Angela is sitting on this horse, but not for long. The horse just bucked its head and before I knew what was happening, I was grovelling in the dirt. Uncle Cecil came striding out of the house.

'Well,' he said, 'you've got to just get straight back up again.'

I was even more terrified, but there was no question of arguing with Uncle Cecil.

'We'll just take it easy on the way out,' he said, 'and to start with I'll take the reins and lead this horse along to steady him up a bit.'

Gradually I gained a little confidence. Not much though, but Cecil said, 'I think you will be okay now. There's not a lot to hit if you do come off, only the dirt.'

I could see that was so but I didn't fancy that again. Uncle Cecil went ahead and my horse went more and more slowly, which became a nightmare of a difference, because the men were all receding into the distance. I didn't have time to look at my surroundings and enjoy the vast acres of paddock and the huge numbers of sheep. My thinking was totally focused on this horse which wouldn't go fast enough to keep up with Uncle Cecil and the men.

They were having a cool drink before starting work on the fences. I was glad to get off the horse and was happy to sit and watch for a while. I was thinking, truly Angela, this is a poor do. They are sure to think I'm pathetic and a nuisance. When they had finished the fencing we all set off for home. I felt a little more confident about it, but Uncle Cecil shouted, 'Sit up straight. Grip with your knees and hold the rein firmly, let the horse know you're in charge.' Some hope, I thought. But I was trying. We headed for home, but this time my horse was in the lead and bolted. I could not pull it up; I just didn't have any effect on this horse at all. Fortunately Uncle Cecil saved me from what could have been a nasty accident. He pulled the horse up and I had to suffer the indignity of being led home.

Another day, Uncle Cecil, who to be fair was trying hard to help me to acclimatise to the country, said, 'What about some driving lessons? This would be a great place to learn. Not a lot to hit, the odd fence and a few thousand sheep, but we can always find an empty paddock. Would you like a go in the truck?'

I said, 'Thank you, that would be great.'

So Uncle Cecil had me climb into the truck, and there I sat behind the wheel. Not fearing him, no, but still a little scared and he did have an abrupt way about him. He went through all about gears and the various procedures I had to learn and then said, 'We'll drive round this paddock and do some turns and reverses.'

I thought, at last this was something I could manage to do. Well, they say pride comes before a fall. A few minutes later Uncle Cecil said, 'I think now you could drive along the track and go over the grid between two lines of fencing.' And I'm driving along, and of course, in my uncertainty, I'm desperately looking at either side of this grid thinking, this truck is not going to go through this gap.

'Look ahead, look ahead,' said Uncle Cecil, 'for God's sake look ahead.'

'Yes,' I said, feebly, and I never forgot that. So while I was up there I had many lessons and lots of practice. It was good of Uncle Cecil to give me the time.

One morning, Aunty Linda said that we'd been invited to friends for dinner. 'Now, Angela, I do hope that you've got something smart to wear with you.'

'Oh yes,' I said, thinking, thank goodness for Aunty Jean's advice.

'A hundred miles,' Aunty Linda said, 'I think it's about a hundred miles.'

I was surprised at this. However, I got all dressed up, strappy high heeled shoes, a very full skirt, and I felt pretty good. Morrie the governess, Barbie, Robb and myself all piled into the back of their car, Cecil driving with Linda beside him, and we set off at wonderful speed. I love going fast. There's nothing of course coming. Lots of grids which were rather bumpy to go over at such high speed, and I thought, well, this isn't going to take us long at all, trying to have a peep at the speedometer, but I couldn't quite see it. The light became very poor and we could hear the rumbling of thunder. Suddenly the rain started. Rain when it happens in a place like that, where they wait so long for it, is torrential. The windscreen wipers were hardly managing to cope. The red dirt became muddier by the minute, and now we were not going fast. In no time at all we were starting to skid. Uncle Cecil said, 'I think we've got trouble here. There's flooding ahead, and I'm not sure if we are going to make this.'

We slithered to a halt and there we were, absolutely stuck, in the middle of nowhere, supposedly going out for dinner, and all dressed up. 'Everybody out,' said Uncle Cecil. And I'm thinking, wow, this is quite something, strappy shoes are not going to be the thing at all. He said, 'You're all going to have to push.' I thought, my shoes, I'll take them off, they're the only decent pair I've got. But my calf-length skirt was impossible to tuck up. We were up to our knees in mud immediately. However, we all pushed and we shoved as best we could, and the car moved a few yards on past the bad bit. We stood there in the rain, soaked and spattered in mud. 'Can't be helped,' said Cecil. 'In you get, and when we get there it'll just have to be a good wash up and lots of apologies.'

The people waiting for us were used to things like this. But for me it added a totally new dimension to a night out. Our hosts were delightful, despite the fact we'd totally wrecked two bathrooms, and they lent us clothes to put on and socks for our feet. It didn't matter at all, we had a great night and were fortunate that the rain, although much needed in vast quantity, didn't last long. So that was good for the journey home.

There was one sad thing at the end of my three weeks. I had a small box Brownie camera. It hadn't cost much, but it seemed to work all right. I'd taken pictures successfully with it so far. I took three spools of photos up at Ercildoune and so looked forward to seeing them. I thought I'd wait until I got back to Sydney to have them developed. Little did I know then that nothing, absolutely none of them, would come out. Such a disappointment, because I never had the chance to go back to Ercildoune, not ever in my whole life, so I have no photographs of those wonderful three weeks there. However, the memories which I have shared with you are still with me now.

It soon came time for me to return to Sydney, and with much regret I said goodbye to the country. Linda, Cecil and family, I would see once more in Sydney, where I had to say goodbye to all my new friends and families, who had given me a fabulous year out. I had no idea when I might see them again, but I was beginning to feel excited about London.

I travelled home on SS *Oronsay* with my grandfather. He had spoken of how he would give me a day on shore when we came alongside Port Suez. Grandpa had arranged for a car to meet us there. We were driven at high speed across the desert to Cairo - exciting! Grandpa had given me strict instructions to keep beside him at all times and to clutch my bag tightly.

He took me first to see the magnificent exhibition in the Cairo Museum, where I was frankly overwhelmed by the gold of the Pharaohs displayed there. Before lunch in a smart hotel, Grandpa and I wandered through the bazaar, which was teeming with people, carts drawn by donkeys or pushed by men old and young. The noise of stall holders plying their wares, the mingling of colours and the heat and dust all gave an air of excitement. I bought a small rug and a leather pouffe seat.

In the afternoon we were driven out of the city to see the Sphinx and the Pyramids. The fierce dry heat and the dust kicked up by camels and horses met us on arrival. Grandpa wisely chose a horse but I was intrigued to try a camel. They stink, and grunt as the small Arab boy prods the camel to kneel down. Keen to do this, I got up on the saddle, only to find that the camel stands up hind legs first, so I was very nearly pitched off over its head! A bad start, but it was a thrill to ride out close to the enormous Pyramids. We looked in awe and amazement, knowing how they had been built by teams of men using only ropes and pulleys with their hands, to move the huge pieces of stone.

Later I persuaded Grandpa, against his better judgment, to let me have a swim to cool off. Not a good idea, as the following day on board ship I became violently ill with dysentery, which lasted for the rest of the voyage. I missed visiting Naples and Marseilles and only managed to crawl on deck to see Gibraltar. A sad end to a fabulous time away.

CHAPTER SEVEN

I had a happy summer at home but I sensed a sadness in my parents, particularly my father, about me going to London. When the time came, I can see it all now at Waverley Station, my luggage, and the family to say goodbye, but my most poignant memory is of Daddy, who after the door had shut and the train had started was moving along the platform shouting at me, 'Remember you can always change your mind.'

We had had a lot of information from the hospital about what it would be like, the uniform – sounded ghastly – and where we should present ourselves on that particular day, early in August 1956. On arrival in London, it was extremely hot. I was wearing a tweed suit. Somehow my mama had her way again, insisting it would be most suitable. Of course, it was most unsuitable for the heat of London. I could hardly bear it, but it was what I had on therefore I just had to put up with it.

The preliminary training school for The Middlesex Hospital was at Lancaster Gate, a number of large houses joined together. We always called it PTS. I was the first to arrive, and as I stood there in the hall surrounded by my luggage, feeling very unsure of myself, in the door came another girl, also far too hot, also in a suit, Lynette Wardby, and she'd come all the way from Kenya. She too was apprehensive, so immediately we struck up a friendship. Others came and we were shown up to our rooms, and told that we should present ourselves downstairs in the sitting room where Sister Slater was going to have a chat to us. It wasn't until we went downstairs and I met the other girls that I realised how smartly dressed they all were, posh hair-dos and immaculate make-up.

Sister Slater explained some of the rules and the plans for our training. Looking around I thought, oh my goodness, everyone seems so sophisticated. However, it wasn't long before Sister Slater said, 'Firstly, we don't allow any make-up and we don't allow lipstick. Secondly, I notice that quite a number of you have beautifully manicured nails with nail polish. The nails must be cut short, and we certainly don't allow nail polish.' There were several people shifting in their seats by this time. 'Thirdly, anyone who has long hair will have to put it right up, securely up. We cannot have hair hanging down over the patients. It would be most unsuitable.'

The room seemed very still. A lot of the girls didn't like this at all. As we came out of the room that first evening, my feelings had reversed again and I was thinking, thank goodness for my short, naturally curly hair. And oh, it doesn't matter about the make-up because I still have quite a bit of suntan. I thought, pity about the lipstick but I suppose we're all in the same boat. Maybe I will fit in after all.

The first morning was a practical one. The sister in charge that morning said, 'I'd like you to go round the entire PTS in pairs. I want every bath, basin and toilet cleaned properly, Now, if any of you have not done it before, somebody is bound to be able to show you how and, if not, one of us will. Nursing is also about working with people, so if you don't know, try and find out from the person with you or someone else, but don't take long about it and we'll be coming round to see how you have done.'

Well, it didn't bother me because I'd helped Mum at home and knew exactly what to do so I thought, that's not difficult. But to some of the girls, the sight of a tin of Gumption and a cloth to go with it, they had no idea. Later, Sister Slater said, 'It's all to do with hygiene. It's no good the doctors treating patients, if you girls, as the nurses, are not going to have everything spotless to keep the germs at bay.'

We were given a timetable of lectures which would be interspersed with group activities such as bandaging. It sound quite a simple task, but I quickly found it was not. I seemed to be all fingers and thumbs, but I wasn't the only one. We lost ten points if we dropped a bandage on the floor. However, that didn't help me to be any better at it and we always used to laugh about it. In fact it was quite a serious matter because we had to learn quickly. We took it in turn to be a patient, taking temperatures, and we made beds for each other, learning hospital corners, etc, and how to give a bed bath and experience what it was like to be given one. Not at all a pleasant feeling, rather cold.

The day came for us to go to the wards. We were each assigned to a different ward. I was sent to the neurological unit, Campbell Thompson. There would be people having serious brain operations and a number of people with chronic nervous diseases. When I arrived, the sister seemed friendly but said quite briskly, 'How about taking the tempcratures, Nurse Wilkie, I think that would do for a start, wouldn't it? Now make sure you are accurate with the charts. If you make a mistake they will have to be redone, and you're far too new to be able to do that.'

'Oh yes, Sister,' I said, thinking to myself, surely I could manage this. I went to the first patient, took the little thermometer out of its pot, looked at it and

Student Nurse Angela Wilkie: The Middlesex Hospital

saw that it needed to be shaken down. Without any worry, I shook it. Unbelievably, it flew right out of my hand. Sister came bustling up.

'Oh dear, well, I suppose these things happen when you're new, I'll get another one out. Try not to do it again, Nurse Wilkie.'

I was covered in confusion; I thought, this is dreadful. I broke three thermometers, one after the other, what a start to my nursing career! I didn't blame the Sister when she said, 'That's the first and last time that you will ever try to take temperatures on my ward.'

After our three months at PTS, we were all transferred to John Astor House, which is the nurses' home. We each had a room to ourselves, only small, it is true, but comfortable and well appointed. There was a tennis court there and a swimming pool for recreation.

After my first ward, I was sent to a women's medical ward called Essex Winter. All over again I felt unsure and shy. This Ward Sister didn't find anything I did suitable or correct. To my astonishment, to my horror and then to my misery, I quickly learned that absolutely everything I did was always wrong. After the first week the Staff Nurse took me aside and said, 'I'm sorry, Nurse Wilkie, but you are it for the moment.'

I said, 'What do you mean?'

She said, 'Well, I'm afraid this particular Ward Sister tends to, as we put it, have a knife into somebody, and you, Nurse Wilkie, are it. It will be like this for the whole six weeks.'

I knew then I would just have to put up with it.

After twelve weeks we moved down to the night nurses' home in Berners Street. Night duty would consist of working from 8 p.m. until 8 a.m., ten nights on and four nights off for three whole months. I was lucky to share a room with my friend Jenny Morris. Jenny lived in Sussex and I'd already been down to stay with her. It was wonderful to be able to get out of London and to stay in someone's home and breathe the fresh air of the countryside. Another friend, Daphne Stanger, whose family lived in Brighton, also had me to stay for nights off: a breath of sea air. Another member of the set with whom I became great friends was Charlotte Rolfe. She had been a PE teacher before she came into nursing. She was a mature, sensible person, like the Rock of Gibraltar. When the rest of us were falling apart, Char would steady us up, talk it through with us and even prevent people from becoming so down that they would think of leaving.

When I presented myself for my first night on Charles Bell Ward, the Staff Nurse came forward in a brisk manner.

'Now, I know it's your first night,' she said, 'and just by looking around you, new as you are, I think you can see that this is a very busy ward. This is a male surgical ward, and it so happens that tonight it is our turn to be on emergency intake.'

My eyes were wider by the minute as I took in the sight of six intravenous drips and so many ill people.

She said, 'I'll give you half an hour of my time, you'd better listen carefully.'

As she introduced me to each patient, she explained about drips, charts, drains and the importance of monitoring. Somehow she had a particular way of encouraging me how to do each task properly without destroying any hope that I might have of achieving it. It is usual to have a seriously ill person nearest to the desk and there was a young man in that particular bed. She introduced me to him and said, 'Nurse Wilkie, this young man has had an operation and we do have to look after him carefully.'

At this point she suggested we should pop outside the curtains for a moment. We went down the ward, out of earshot.

She continued, 'This is extremely important. You heard in the report that this gentleman has had an operation in his groin. We are concerned that the stitches might not hold and he may have a serious haemorrhage from his femoral artery. If it is going to happen, Nurse Wilkie, it is most likely to happen when you, as the junior, are making him comfortable and turning him on his side. Don't worry, I'm going to tell you what to do. Make a fist of your hand, and push it into his groin and hold it there – this will staunch the blood – and then shout. Don't try to ring the bell, you more than likely won't be able to reach it. Keep your fist where I have told you and shout for help.'

Well, I thought, it all sounds rather dramatic, but surely it isn't going to happen.

I managed to get through the evening drinks, although I found it particularly difficult to make Horlicks for the men who wished it. I had no idea that you were meant to mix it first to a paste with the cold milk, and then put the hot milk in afterwards, and I struggled with this huge pan of hot milk that had to be poured into jugs and the likelihood of it boiling over or burning. I got through the round of the back-rubbing and making people comfortable. And then I came to the young man by the desk. He was quite cheerful although he was still very ill, and I wasn't at all concerned. So I turned him on his side, and literally as I did that the haemorrhage started. Everything I did then was completely automatic. Thanks to that excellent Staff Nurse, I made a fist out of my hand, I pushed it into his groin and I shouted. A houseman pushed his head round the corner of the curtain and said, 'Oh my goodness, I thought you were new.'

'Well, I am,' I said.

Then he said, 'Good for you, hold on, I'll get the necessary help.'

It was amazing – that could have been very serious if I had not known what to do. As it was, I didn't feel the new girl at all now. And then of course, after the event, I found that I could gain confidence from having coped in a difficult situation.

During this time, our family business, Wilkie's, brought my father to London regularly to see the fashion collections. He'd bring the buyers down with him and Daddy would quite often ask me if I would like to come along to one of the shows. I found that a great delight, and I truly sat in wonderment at how the buyer would sit through an entire show and then order these different clothes, in different colours and sizes, and seemed to know exactly what would be right for the customers back in Scotland.

There were several other pluses. Daddy always stayed at the Berners Hotel, almost next door to York House. During my time in London, there's no doubt about it, we had the time to talk together and share all sorts of things. He would take me out for dinner and dancing. I'd get all dressed up, and we'd go to somewhere like the Trocadero, or even Hatchetts. My father was a wonderful dancer and I adored it; he really taught me to dance well. I think sometimes people thought he was a 'sugar daddy', and I was some girl he picked up. We used to laugh about it.

But I also learned why Daddy used to go away at weekends and why Mum would then be stressed and worried. We knew it was something to do with needing medical treatment, but we never knew what. Even when I went to London and did know that Daddy had this depressive illness, it wasn't until my training gave me a sensitivity and some knowledge of these things that I was able to understand. Knowing as I did after some of my nursing lectures what electric shock treatment entailed, and what that meant for Daddy, horrified me, and also certain parts of the jigsaw fell into place. I had never understood why, when Daddy came back from Melrose, he couldn't remember anything from just a few days before. But that is what the treatment was doing to him, while bringing out all the trouble and stress he'd been through during the war. So Daddy and I became very, very close during my years in London, and what had been a terrible wrench for him became a happiness for us both.

CHAPTER EIGHT

Another change took me to the first floor, Princess Alice Ward. This was a combination of a special eye unit and a ward for past and present nurses who needed hospital care. In the three months that I worked there I learned of the sensitive nursing care required for patients who had had eye operations. This often entailed them being confined to bed for up to three weeks, lying absolutely flat and still. We had to give them every sip of fluid and every mouthful of food and somehow keep their spirits up.

I remember one day being asked to help in the theatre where the eye operations were taking place. The eye surgeon was a tall, large man with huge hands and I, as the junior, had been asked to hold the lamp. They didn't have lamps that came down from the ceiling, and clever things as they do nowadays. My difficulty was that I felt the surgeon's hands were always in the way, but it was my job to find a way for the light to shine exactly where he wanted it, somehow around his hands. Quite a test it was, that. In fact it kept me a hundred per cent concentrating on what I was doing. Another day when I was in the theatre, just observing, I realised that I found eye surgery quite upsetting to watch. People often say that theatres are glamorous – I didn't find that. For me, theatres were not places where I wanted to work. I liked best the person to person, patient to nurse relationship. Not all those instruments and the clinically sterile unit: an unreal world, as if the patients were not people.

After a period in block to study, I was sent with others in my set to work at the Soho Women's Hospital in Soho Square, which was part of The Middlesex Hospital. 'Gynae' – most people said they hated it. I wasn't sure what to expect. The patients' ages ranged from young girls who sadly had had a back street abortion and had come to the hospital in a dreadful state, to the very elderly women who needed a repair operation and should have had it twenty years before, but had put up with all the discomfort and the problems that a prolapse had given them. I came face to face with women whose marriages had gone wrong, whose husbands beat them. I hadn't come across anything like this in my life until that time in Soho Hospital, but there I saw the results of every degree of abuse to women and every gynaecological problem you could think of.

Soho Hospital was old fashioned, with highly polished ward floors – dangerous, I used to think. Being a small hospital made it more personal. We had Christmas there. Giving those women a happy Christmas was tremendous fun for us, since we knew that most of them had never known what happiness was. I felt that women in that situation needed so much more than just the medical and basic nursing care, and I enjoyed trying to give them that, to listen when they needed to talk things over. Many of them had a great need to share problems. The availability of counselling that there is nowadays was not even thought of in the same way, and the little that there was would not have come the way of these women.

I stayed with women for my next move, but this time it was to the maternity ward. I truly looked forward to this. I'd always adored babies, tiny ones I mean, but I had never seen one born. Having two sisters much younger than myself had given me a lot of opportunity to help my mother when they were babies. There is something so special about even the smell of a baby. Everything about them is fascinating – the way their little noses wrinkle, and their mouths move up and down, when they are asleep. The wonder of a new-born baby has never left me, and my time on maternity at The Middlesex instilled in me a strong wish to do my midwifery training. We were trained to understand not only the wonder and excitement of a new-born baby after all that pain and difficulty, but also to sense and understand the real problems that most new mums had. How inadequate and inept they felt.

Being student nurses in such a specialised unit, they taught us several things by observation only, so that we were allowed to go and watch the delivery of a baby, but of course not to assist at it. It was a very emotional experience to see a little one come into the world, but sadly it was sometimes mixed with worry and stress because something might be wrong with the baby: another huge area of sensitivity for midwives and nurses to cope with.

One evening, I was alone in the nursery as I'd been asked by the Staff Nurse to feed one of the tiny babies every two hours. I wasn't worried about doing this because I'd been in the nursery lots of times with the Staff Nurse when she had fed this baby herself. I picked the baby out of her cot; I made sure the bottle was warm and she seemed to be taking the feed well. Suddenly she choked and her colour changed to blue and then to white. In a flash I held her up by her ankles and slapped her hard on her bottom, lower back and slightly higher. It was a completely instinctive reaction – there wasn't time to think or decide what to do or how to do it. I just did it. Thank goodness. I remember walking round the nursery, holding her close and watching her colour come back, and thinking of the responsibility of the work that I was training to do. Once the baby seemed to be breathing fine, I wrapped her up carefully, laid her down in the cot, and went smartly along the corridor - not allowed to run of course. It's amazing how fast you can walk when you need to - to get the Staff Nurse. She came straight along and while we went back to the nursery, I told her what had happened.

'Don't worry, Nurse Wilkie,' she said, 'you did fine.'

'Yes,' I said, 'but it might not have been all right.' I felt the nursery was so far away from everyone.

'Well, there is a bell in the nursery here, Nurse Wilkie, there is a bell, you should have rung that.'

Of course, but in my stress I hadn't thought of that.

After a long weekend in Edinburgh for my twenty-first birthday, it was back to London. I was now in my third year. We all passed the exams and were wearing what they called 'strings'. These, would you believe it, were long pieces of highly starched material which we had to fold into a narrow strip that would meet under the chin in the shape of a fluted bow. Achieving this wretched bow in the middle of these strings took ages to do, then to have to wear them under your chin - nobody would tolerate them nowadays. It was extremely uncomfortable, scratchy, awful, hot, but of course to begin with we were so proud to be wearing them. Wearing our strings increased our responsibilities immediately; it was a position we'd looked forward to but were to find daunting at times.

That particular winter, there was a serious situation in The Middlesex Hospital, in fact throughout Great Britain - a dreadful flu epidemic. One by one, patients, nurses, and medical and ancillary staff succumbed to it. Those of us left had four times as much work to do. I had kept extremely well throughout my training apart from the odd infection but now I wasn't feeling good. I kept saying it was so hot in the hospital. Of course, I was running a temperature. But there wasn't time to be worried about that sort of thing, because literally there was Sister and myself left in the Observation Ward. Some of the rooms were empty and we were not taking any new patients, but even that didn't help the fact that the two of us were on our knees trying to cope. What made this particular unit difficult to cover was that it had many separate rooms, but we soldiered on until one day when it got to lunch time, and the lunch trolley arrived. I thought, how am I going to take this through to these people? I have never felt so poorly in my whole life.

Sister took one look at me and said, 'Nurse Wilkie, you have got to go off. I know I need you, and I know there won't be a replacement coming, but you will not be standing up, you will just be another patient. I can't handle another patient, so if you don't mind, go off and report to the sick bay.'

Two weeks later I wasn't fit for much but felt I should go back on duty since you wouldn't have dreamt of staying off longer than you had to. We had vital exams to do at this time and I was finding the studying more difficult because I felt so tired when I came off duty. The format for exams was to take the state registration ones first to achieve our SRN followed by the hospital exams which we were assured would be more difficult. I wanted to stay on as a Staff Nurse, and without those two exams I knew that I wouldn't be given that opportunity. I suppose that my best help for those exams was my experience with the patients themselves. I think when it came to the crunch and I turned the piece of paper over and read the questions, it was a certain person at a certain time with a particular problem, which gave me the ability to write down what was necessary. I think that without the reality of looking after all these people during three years of training, the knowledge from books and listening to lectures would not have been sufficient.

After the exams I was assigned to the Woolavington Private Wing. I was delighted to be going there. It intrigued me, and I wondered how different it would be. I was assigned to a four-bedded room on the ground floor which had large French windows looking onto the garden. There were polished floors and comfortable chintzy chairs with bedspreads and curtains to match, and excellent food from the kitchen. But of course the people were expecting the very best.

A great friend of mine, Sally Sinclair, was also on Woolavington at the same time as me and a buzz had gone round that Sir Winston Churchill was a patient with us. It was meant to be a secret, of course, but I knew from Sally that he was on her floor. One day she asked me if I would like to come and meet Sir Winston? Naturally I said I would love to, but how on earth would we manage that?

'Oh, it's quite easy,' she said. 'You come up to the floor to borrow something. I'm in and out of his room all the time. You'll hardly be able to see him for the smoke. Come around lunch time when Sister is off.'

We should not have been doing it. It was unprofessional and indiscreet, but it was such an opportunity to see the great man, whom we all admired. The following day, I nipped upstairs and there was Sally, who does appear to be quite shy usually, but there she was full of confidence. She went straight along the corridor and I meekly followed behind. Sally knocked on a particular door, and in we went. She was right, the grey haze of choking smoke hit our eyes and lungs, but there, in bed, was Sir Winston Churchill, propped up on a mountain of pillows, not breathing very well and smoking a large cigar. I was thrilled to be in that room. Sally didn't introduce me of course, that was quite out of the question. She spoke to Sir Winston about one or two things and we sorted his pillows together before we left. I know I didn't speak to him, but it was special for me to have even been in the same room as Sir Winston Churchill.

From Woolavington, I was assigned to Queen Alexandra Ward for my third year night duty, an acute women's medical ward where the consultants specialised in diabetes and endocrinology. It sounded pretty complicated to me. Although a medical floor, we gave immediate post-operative care to patients who had had serious operations pertaining to the adrenal or pituitary glands. I found endocrinology a fascinating subject and adored working on that floor. It was challenging, often difficult, harrowing even, but most rewarding because it brought together the many skills which I'd learned throughout my nursing training. We had an excellent houseman there, Sidney Crown was his name, not good looking, but a delightful guy who was much more mature than any houseman I'd met so far.

One night we were caring for a patient with an intracaval drip. I knew how important it was to monitor this patient frequently. I was going to the treatment room, but stopped at the patient's bed and noted that the bottle of fluid was more than half full. I continued on up the ward to collect one or two instruments and returned immediately. Out of habit, I looked up at the drip, and I couldn't believe it. The bottle was absolutely empty! I turned the tap off and ran to the telephone. Absolutely ran, terrified that an air bubble would give the patient an embolism. Although it appeared that I had been careless, I knew that I had not. I got Sidney, who came running down to the ward with a large syringe to draw out any air that may have gone down the tubing, and what a relief to find that it hadn't gone far at all. That was a bad five minutes, a dreadful sinking feeling a weight of responsibility of what I felt I had done, or rather allowed to happen. Many nurses may have similar incidents in their careers. Things do happen which are outwith our control. At the same time, as the person in charge, one would have to carry the can for it. I was fortunate not to have to do that.

The ward was so busy and interesting that night duty was absolutely flying by. I especially enjoyed the early hours of the morning when, up on the third floor there, you could watch the dawn breaking over London.

I had received an invitation from my brother's girlfriend's family, the Clarks, to their elder daughter Gillian's twenty-first birthday dinner dance at their home in Epsom. They had already kindly entertained me and I'd got to know them. Judy, Alexander's girlfriend, was doing nursing at St Bartholomew's Hospital, so we had a lot in common. I was invited to stay for a couple of nights after the party. They had a house full of young people which gave a great buzz of excitement to it all.

With that sort of party, it was the custom to be introduced to people, and in fact I thought I had met everybody. After the speeches for Gillian's birthday, Mr Clark announced that it was time to go into dinner. There was a great crush of people around the dining table and as my turn came to pick up a plate and help myself to Mrs Clark's wonderful food, I almost tripped over somebody who was kneeling on the floor, right in front of the vol-au-vents. I couldn't remember being introduced to him.

He stood up and said, 'Hello, I'm John Dobbie.'

I said, 'Oh, I'm Angela Wilkie – you are obviously enjoying those.'

'Oh, they're my favourite thing,' he continued.

'Well, I don't suppose there will be many left for anyone else!'

That sounded a bit mean of me, but I thought, how greedy can you get. After dinner there was dancing and I discovered that this young man I had just tripped over was a fabulous dancer.

CHAPTER NINE

Although I'd had such a wonderful night at Gillian's party, after which John said he would give me a call sometime, the weeks had gone by and I hadn't heard anything, and quite honestly didn't expect to. So one day when a nurse knocked on my door at John Astor House to say there was a phone call for me downstairs, I couldn't imagine who it was. When I went down I was amazed that it was John. He invited me out for a drink and I said that would be fine. We talked about my off-duty and arranged a time for him to pick me up.

The day arrived and I can remember what I wore: a blue cotton skirt and a blue and white striped sailor type v-neck sleeveless top, with white sandals. It was a very hot evening. I went downstairs to the entrance hall of John Astor House and sank into one of those dark green velvet sofas by the front door where people waited for friends. Sure enough, John walked in the door and off we went in his old Ford 10 car. He drove down to a pub I'd never been to, although I had heard of it, the Prospect of Whitby, down by the river, and we had a few drinks there, and I must say I enjoyed myself tremendously. We seemed to hit it off. We had lots of laughs because John has a great sense of humour, and the evening went by in a flash. When he brought me back to the Nurses' Home, he invited me to go out again sometime, and when I said that would be fine, he said he would give me a ring. When I went upstairs to my room and flopped down on my bed, I thought, wow, that was a truly good night. I really liked this guy. I felt singingly happy.

A week or so later John rang me and invited me to go to rather a posh do down in Epsom at the Royal Automobile Club. He said I would need a formal dress as it was a dinner dance, and I thought, okay, I could handle that. He explained that he was going to be playing hockey in North London for his firm, Shell International, and that he was going to be driving up through London and would pick me up on the way back and then very kindly take me all the way to the Nurses' Home afterwards since I was due on duty at 7.30 a.m. It was a very happy evening but went all too quickly. By the time we got back to London, John was absolutely exhausted. I went upstairs and fell into bed, knowing that I had to go on duty the next morning, and John drove back home to Epsom.

Somehow I woke up in time to go on duty but couldn't wait for 1.30 p.m. when I could go off again. All I wanted to do was sleep. I was exhausted but when I got back to my room, having had a snack, someone told me there had been a phone call for me. Somebody called John, they thought. I thought it strange, I would have thought he would be asleep. Then they said it was from Epsom District Hospital. I couldn't get to the phone quickly enough, dialled the hospital and enquired how John Dobbie was. They said they would put him on the line.

I said, 'John, what on earth are you doing in hospital?'

A rather muffled voice from the other end said, 'Well, I drove into a lamp-post on the way home. I nearly made it but I went to sleep at the wheel – thank goodness for the chassis of the old Ford 10, because otherwise – curtains.'

I said, 'You sound awfully peculiar. Why are you allowed to the telephone?'

He said, 'Well, I bit my tongue very badly and I have hurt my knee.'

I thought, 'Oh help!' I told him I would be right down to see him.

Gone were my feelings of exhaustion, tiredness and wanting to sleep. I thought, right, get changed and catch a train down to see him, thinking the poor guy must be absolutely miserable. When I arrived some hours later, I was shown up to the ward and there was John, despite his bad knee and the car smash, chasing one of the nurses round the ward with a face cloth, a rather wet one, I thought. He'd obviously been very lucky, but I think he was quite pleased to see me, and I realised that the worst of the damage had been done to his tongue. You can't really stitch a tongue and it is extremely painful. He couldn't eat much, even drinking was sore. But it could all have been much worse. The chassis of that old car had surely saved him.

John was in for a couple of nights. Then he was back to work with Shell which was based at St Helen's Court in the City of London. He was travelling up from Epsom from his mother's home every day on the train so it was easy for us to meet each other. Suddenly London became a more exciting place for me, with new experiences all the time.

We shared many interests. A love of music, both classical and jazz, the theatre and of course the dancing, but above all there was golf. We would take off with a picnic and our clubs in the back of his new old car, this time a Morris Minor convertible. How I loved it when the roof was down and I could feel the wind blowing through my hair.

About this time I was moving into a flat with my girlfriends, Jenny, Gwyn, Meg, Sally and Helen. John soon got to know them and I got to know his mother, Mrs Madge Dobbie, and his brother Peter. I went often to the Dobbies' and always felt very much at home there. Peter picked up on my name being Angela Wilkie, and before I knew it, he had nicknamed me Wilk the Whelk and it has stuck all these years.

Meanwhile I'd come off night duty and was thrilled to have passed both the state registration and the hospital exams. We'd been summoned in turn to Miss Marriott's office and offered Staff Nurse positions in different wards, and to my delight I was offered the position of Staff Nurse on Queen Alex where I'd just finished my third night duty. I was absolutely thrilled. We had to keep the same boring uniform – the tan dress, the white apron – but instead of the tan belt, the one thing we did aspire to as a Staff Nurse was a navy blue belt. You could say not a lot different, but indeed it was. I think we felt we'd arrived when we had that navy belt around our middle. On my first day as I was bounding upstairs, Miss Marriott and Brigadier Hardy Roberts, the administrator of the hospital, were coming down. To my amazement they stopped and Miss Marriott said, 'Congratulations, Miss Wilkie,' and Brigadier Hardy Roberts said, 'I hope you're going to be very happy on Queen Alex; we're so delighted that you're taking the position.' I felt they made it personal. It added a wonderful touch to that day when I started on Queen Alex.

When I arrived on the ward, I already knew many of the patients. Sister Mackie and I sat down at the desk to have the report. It was a Friday lunchtime and she was going for her weekend off. It was not only going to be my first day as a Staff Nurse but also my first weekend in charge on my own. I didn't know whether to be excited or scared; it was all mixed up together. No, I wasn't scared, I welcomed it. Because I knew the unit well already I was hopeful that I could cope with whatever situation presented itself.

During the report Sister particularly mentioned Jane, a young girl of fifteen who was in a bed at the far end of the ward. She had severe acute bacterial endocarditis and had been in the ward for nine weeks. She had done wonderfully well on the injections of penicillin which she'd been having and although she was painfully thin and still weak, she was going to a convalescent home the following day. We were all thrilled for her. Sister Mackie explained that Jane hadn't been too good that morning, but everything was set for her journey the next day and we were just keeping a close eye on her. Sister went off and I thought, well, this is a large family I've inherited. All these patients are going to depend on me.

I started at the first bed and thought, I'll do a round and have a little word with each patient. I came to Jane's bedside. I took one look at her, I felt her pulse. I couldn't believe it. I couldn't feel it. There was no pulse. She was just lying there with her eyes shut, her long dark hair spread out on the pillow. So peaceful she looked and yet I knew she was gone.

I quietly drew the curtains round the bed and walked slowly down the ward.

I could see the visitors standing outside the door of the ward, as usual impatiently wanting to come in. I looked at my watch. It was only 2.15 p.m. Officially they weren't supposed to come in until 2.30 p.m. I went through the doors, said 'Good afternoon,' and walked straight past them to the telephone in the big linen room and dialled Sidney Crown, the Houseman, to tell him what had happened. I walked slowly back, knowing I would have to face the barrage of visitors, but there was something much worse. I knew that Jane's parents would be among this group of eager visitors. They would be carrying her suitcase with all her things ready to go to the convalescent home. They were already happy that she was feeling better. They were looking forward to having her out of the main hospital and into the country.

I explained to the visitors that the ward was not quite ready and apologised for the delay, then I went back into the ward. I beckoned to the nurses to come to the desk and I asked them all to sit down. I said, 'This is very difficult and I've got to tell you something hard, and you've all got to be very brave. Jane has just slipped away, she has died suddenly and peacefully.' The most junior nurse covered her eyes with her hands and I said, 'Now, we have got to hold on. The patients are watching us and the visitors are right behind us at the door. We've got to be brave and carry on, for everyone's sake. Each of you can play your part and get the patients ready as quickly as possible. I've got to speak to Jane's parents.'

I think that helped them to pull themselves together, knowing that dreadful job lay ahead of me. To be truthful I didn't have any idea how I was going to do it.

The nurses stood up quietly, carried on and to their credit they didn't give any indication of what had happened. By this time Sidney had come into the ward and, with just a glance at myself, he'd walked straight up the ward and, after examining Jane, returned to the desk. Then we both went outside to the office.

Sidney said, 'This is awful and very sad, but it can happen like that. A tiny piece of the endocarditis breaks off and in a moment becomes an embolism. Fifteen is so young.'

I told Sidney that her parents were right here and I thought he would tell them, surely he would tell them. But he said, 'No, Angela, I think it would be better if you do it. You know them better than myself.'

'But Sidney, surely it's your place, you are the doctor,' I said.

'That's true,' he said, 'but I've got another patient to see urgently on the men's ward, and I must go to that situation. We can't tell them later, we've got to tell them now. Do your best.' And with that he went out of the door.

It was too awful for words. I went to the group of visitors and said, 'We're nearly ready now; may I have a quick word with Jane's mum and dad while the rest of you go through.'

They came into Sister's office and sat down, looking at me eagerly, thinking it was to do with travel arrangements for the following day. There isn't any easy way to say something so difficult. And I didn't try to wrap it up at all. I just said, 'We've all had the most awful shock and it is an awful shock. Jane has died peacefully, about five minutes before you came to the ward.'

They looked at me, the eager expectation crumbling in their faces. They couldn't speak so I just explained gently how I had walked to her bed and was beside her and that she'd just gone to sleep. I said, 'She looked so lovely and peaceful and she didn't have any pain at all. I'm sorry about it being visitors, it's such a difficult time. Would you like to stay here for a little while, or would you like to come with me now and be with Jane, just sit beside her?'

They wanted to be with her. They stood up very slowly, turned towards the door, hardly seeing it and I took them quietly up the ward which was now busy and bustling with the noises of visiting time, up to the bed on the left where the curtains were drawn. I took them inside and I brought them a couple of chairs. They sat either side of Jane holding her hands and I left them there.

Sidney came back to the ward. I was sitting at the desk, not doing anything, just sitting there. Not seeing anything, or looking at anything, just being. He sat down beside me. 'It is tough, Angela,' he said.

'Yes,' I answered. I didn't seem to have anything else to say; I couldn't, I was absolutely choked. But I had to control my emotion and be strong. Everyone was depending on me. It was a very, very long afternoon and the evening seemed even longer, trying to keep up the nurses' spirits which were just as low as mine. A terribly sad day, my first day as a Staff Nurse.

We had many very ill patients on the ward, some with serious diabetic problems. The consultant on the diabetic side was Dr Nabarro - not the politician of those days, but his brother. He was an Australian, a short stocky man with a bristly moustache, dark hair, very dark beady eyes, a rather impatient manner and a quick way of walking. But he was excellent with the patients. He would take a lot of time to find out about their home and personal circumstances. Dr Nabarro was very forward in his thinking. His investigations entailed a vast number of tests. But these tests were giving us a problem at the far end of the ward, namely, in the sluice.

Both Sister and I had been saying to the Houseman and Registrar that we had no more space to keep specimen jars. One Saturday morning Dr Nabarro was doing his round accompanied by his usual entourage. I decided that he was a man to call a spade a spade, and that I ought to be open and confront him with the problem that we had. When the round was coming to its conclusion, I said, 'Could I have a word, sir?' - to which he agreed. I don't know why I chose to say it in front of all those people, but suddenly it just came out and I said, 'Well sir, the fact is there's a problem at the far end of the ward, in the sluice, where with the best will in the world there is not sufficient space to put another specimen jar. Either we will have to delay some tests, or . . .'

'Well, Staff,' he interrupted, 'I think we should get right down there and have a look at this.'

You could see the faces of the students, not to mention the Senior Registrar and Houseman: what did Staff Nurse Wilkie think she was doing? Before they knew it, Dr Nabarro, with me in tow and all of them following behind, swept down the full length of Queen Alex and into the sluice. There wasn't room for even a quarter of them in the sluice - they waited outside. After a quick glance at the situation Dr Nabarro turned round and said, 'Quite right, Staff, this is ridiculous. I'll see to this. I'm sure we can't be needing all of these for such a long time.'

With that he turned round, went down the ward and out of the main doors. The students followed him but the Senior Registrar and Houseman stayed by the desk. 'Well, Staff, it looks as if we are the ones who are going to be in trouble now.' Of course they were. There were a number of people who had been kept on the tests long after it was necessary, simply because the doctors were hoping to have an answer to every question Dr Nabarro might ask them.

CHAPTER TEN

Ever since I'd been on the maternity wing in The Middlesex Hospital, I'd decided that I wanted to do midwifery. I had planned to do it at the Simpson Memorial Maternity Pavilion in Edinburgh so I booked myself in to do a year's training there, but now since I was having such a good time down south with John, I was regretting that decision. But there was nothing for it really.

I returned to Edinburgh, and the family were great. They were happy to see me, even if I wasn't quite so happy to be there. I did look forward very much to doing my 'midder' training at the Simpson which I believed to be the best in the country at the time, and I would just have to cope with my private feelings, missing John and the wonderful time that I'd been sharing with him. It was a shock though to find out that we would have to live in the Florence Nightingale Home, as they called it, which belonged to the Royal Infirmary. But everything about the work was excellent; I just adored it.

I started off in the ante-natal ward but there was a lot of sadness there. People imagine that everything to do with babies is a happiness. Sadly, this is not so. There at the Simpson, which is the top unit in Scotland, we looked after many difficult situations which required specialist care. Women who were trying hard to have a baby but constantly losing them. Others who were trying to have one, and were finding out that maybe they were never going to manage it. Others who had to come and be in hospital and stay in bed for weeks, sometimes months, to keep their baby. All these were aspects of nursing, but again I found it drew on the experiences that I'd had in the past four years at The Middlesex with people. It's all about people of course. It's not just technique, people need empathy.

It was awful living in the Florence Nightingale Nurses' Home where we were treated in many ways as if we were young schoolgirls again. On the wards we were often given considerable responsibility but in the Nurses' Home, run by these women in green uniforms whom we christened the green lizards, we were treated appallingly, unnecessarily so.

One night, when I first started a session of night duty, I came downstairs to have breakfast at 7 p.m., and one of these ladies came forward and said,

'Aren't you Nurse Wilkie?' I said that I was. 'Oh,' she said, 'there was a phone call for you from London.'

I was so excited, wonderful. I said, 'Which call box is it?'

She looked up. 'Oh,' she said, 'it was ages ago. You can't have phone calls here, you know.'

I was speechless, aghast, miserable, furious, seething, all mixed up. I thought, this is the most beastly, unreasonable place, there's no need for this. I stormed into breakfast and I sat down with my friends who were also coming on night duty. They were moaning as usual about the breakfast. Well, it was probably the least bad of meals presented at the place, but there was so much discontent, and somehow, in my mind anyway, this was the last straw. I thought, it's ridiculous how people like ourselves are just accepting this treatment in the Nurses' Home, when we were being treated with respect on the wards. I stood up, having not eaten my breakfast, I had no appetite for anything, I was so upset and angry, and said, 'I'm going to see Matron.'

As I swept out, everyone just looked at me, amazed. I said, 'It's ridiculous, we're all unhappy, we're all moaning, I think someone needs to speak up and it should be discussed, instead of all this discontent brewing.'

I left the dining room, I went along the hall and out of the door, and as I strode briskly towards the main building and Matron's office, one of the Night Sisters was coming in the other direction.

'Nurse Wilkie, what is the matter?' she said.

'I'm going to see Matron,' I said. 'We are all absolutely fed up and somebody has got to speak to her and represent the others.'

'Oh,' she said, 'please, Nurse Wilkie, don't go now, don't go while you are feeling like this.'

I wouldn't heed her at all. 'I'm going now, I have to go now,' I said.

Of course, in my anger and upset, I was forgetting the time. Matron would hardly be there at 7.20 a.m., and even if the office was open it would be a surprise. I was not deterred by these thoughts. I swept right on into the main building, and into the administration part where a secretary was putting her coat on.

I said, 'I want to see the Matron please. I need to see her now, it's urgent.'

'Oh,' she said, 'I'm sorry, you can't see her now. The Matron, Miss Taylor, is on holiday. She has just gone on holiday and will be away for three weeks. In any case, if you want to see her you need to make an appointment and state what it is you wish to speak to her about.'

Deflated, I stood there and thought, I'm going to have to be extremely patient. There's nothing for it. So I sat down and I wrote, as briefly as possible, a list of things which I felt were causing all the discontent, and asked if I might speak with Miss Taylor about these matters on her return.

The secretary was very nice. She said, 'I'll make you an appointment; I could pencil you in.'

'Thank you,' I said, in a very meek and small voice.

Well, those three weeks seemed forever. It's true I was busy but I didn't feel any less uptight. We were all still discontented. So when the day dawned, I felt excited again. I thought, at last we're going to sort this out, and things might improve. I went across at the appointed time and waited patiently outside Miss Taylor's room. I knocked on her door. 'Come,' she said. I walked in, calmly and slowly, and I stood in front of her large desk. Miss Taylor was reading my letter. She looked up and said, 'Nurse Wilkie, we have nothing to discuss.'

I couldn't believe it. I turned round and ever so slowly and quietly opened the door, walked through it, and turned round and shut it so softly, when in myself I wanted to slam it.

Eventually I was moved to work on the labour suite itself. There I had my best chance to deliver a baby for the first time, under strict supervision. Unfortunately I disgraced myself once on the labour suite, when a mother was about to go into the second stage of labour. I suddenly couldn't see. My new contact lenses were all misted up. I said to the Sister, 'I'm sorry I'm going to have to be excused for a moment.'

'Be excused, Nurse Wilkie,' she said, 'don't be so ridiculous, we're delivering a baby here. What do you mean be excused?' She was quite rightly furious.

'I can't see, I'm sorry, it's my contact lenses.'

'It's your vanity, young lady,' she said, 'get out of my sight and don't come near our labour suite with contact lenses ever again.'

I crept out of the door, her words ringing in my ears as I went to the nurses' cloakroom. I felt truly ashamed and worried that they would never have me back to work on the labour suite. I felt labelled, that stupid, vain nurse who can't be relied upon. I can assure you, I never wore my contact lenses again when working.

Things got better and I experienced many happy weeks on the labour suite, during which I was now allowed to deliver several babies and be present at Caesarean and forceps deliveries.

I was then appointed to go to Ward 53. I didn't know what that would mean, but I soon found out. Ward 53 meant Sister Jenkins, Sister Jenks we called her, or just Jenks. This Sister was an outstanding lady, I felt. She organised and you could say ruled the entire unit – the wards for the mothers, the single rooms, the nurseries, the kitchens and even the bathrooms. She and Doctor Kennedy, the Consultant Obstetrician, were like-minded; they made an excellent team and they ran a happy unit.

About that time, it had been decided throughout the hospital to have what they called 'rooming in'. This was to mean that the babies, instead of being in the nurseries, were going to be in their little cots beside the mothers in the wards all the time, day and night. The reason given for this decision was that it was believed it would cut down the infection rate. Sister Jenkins and Doctor Kennedy were one hundred per cent opposed to it and they would not have this new policy on their unit; they dug their heels in and they refused to change. So when I arrived on 53, the babies were in their cots in the nursery. The babies went in to the mothers many times during the day, but for all meals, rests and at nights the babies were looked after in the nursery.

We were extremely busy working on the ward but I loved it and admired Sister Jenkins, a slightly built lady with sandy coloured hair and glasses, crisp looking but with warm eyes. She had warned me on one of my first days working in one of the nurseries that all eighteen babies as well as names had personalities. Even if they're only a few hours or a day old, they will rule the nursery and you will be running round in circles.

Although I was loving my midder training, and I had booked myself in to do the entire first and second parts there, at the Simpson, I was missing John very much and I was seriously considering the idea, which was an option in those days though not now, of doing my second part, district midwifery, down in England. 'What a stupid idea,' my mother said. 'For goodness sake, don't do that. You're all organised to do it here at the Simpson which is the best place.'

I was not deterred and found out that I could get into the Epsom District Hospital in Surrey, very near John's home, to do my second part, district midwifery nursing, there. I felt that if there was a way where I could combine my training with personal happiness, I should go for it.

Going down to Epsom Hospital was another new stage, totally different from the Simpson. A couple of months of working on the maternity unit there and yet more lectures were followed by the best bit of all, being on the district. Diana Goodliff and I were teamed up as pupil midwives for the Sutton District under the wing of Miss White, the midwife. The idea was that Di and I would take alternate cases but as it turned out, Di had every day case and I had all the night ones. Sutton was built on a hill. The posh houses were at the top, and Diana seemed to be delivering all the babies in these homes, while I was delivering the babies at the bottom of the hill, where the poorer families stayed, and I most certainly had the best time. I felt at home in the town of Sutton as it was then – it's grown so much now – it was amazing how quickly you seemed to get to know so many people working on the district.

We were meant to ride around on our bicycles although, of course, Nurse

White had a car, and at night she did always take me out in her car, but that particular winter of 1961/62 was so severe, with ice packed on top of the snow, that there was no way we could cycle. Nurse White looked after us. When I had been out on a night visit with her, which meant she was doing both days and nights, we'd come in very tired and the rule was always to unpack, sterilise and repack your case before you relaxed at all, in case you were suddenly called out again. And often we were so tired she would say, 'Oh don't you worry, I'll just do it in a moment, it won't take me long.' She spoilt us in that way. I mean, we did often do it ourselves, but she was extremely good to Di and me, and it was such a happy time.

One day Nurse White received a call from one of the doctors to say that he would like us to visit a patient whom he'd seen that morning at his surgery. He explained that he thought her pregnancy was full-term but he was appalled that she had not sought ante-natal care until that day. He said she was a highly intelligent lady with two children of six and four; both she and her husband had been at university, but they were in a sad situation. Miss White said she'd like me to go with her. When we arrived at the house, this tall lady with long bedraggled hair answered the door and we could see she was already in labour. We went through with her and made her comfortable on her bed, and after Miss White had examined her, she said, 'I think she will be a while yet. Get everything ready for this delivery, Nurse Wilkie, and look out things for the baby. I've got to go and see another lady down the road but I won't be that long. Just hold the fort here.'

Well, it seemed as if Miss White had only just shut the front door when this mother was saying, 'Nurse, I've got to push.' And I'm thinking, I haven't even got my bag open. But midwifery is like that: babies aren't going to wait for anything to be made ready. At that moment I experienced the enormous responsibility of delivering a baby in somebody's home, entirely on my own. Luckily, as these things often are in such a quick situation, it was an easy delivery, and my bag was there and I managed fine. Having attended to the mum and baby as best I could and tucked them up together in the large double bed, I turned round to see two wee faces peeping round the door.

'Would you like to come and see your baby sister?' I said. They came rushing in, and gave their mum and the baby a lovely big hug. Meanwhile I was taking in the fact that these two little children were freezing, dressed only in tee-shirts and shorts; they didn't even have shoes or socks on. I couldn't believe it.

Leaving them all there together, I went through the house, thinking that somewhere there would be the things laid out for the baby. I couldn't find anything at all. Not a cot, or nappies, or anything that looked as if it had been a nursery for the other two. I went back into the bedroom, and gently asked the mother where she had some things for the baby. Could she tell me, and I would get them.

She looked away. 'I've sold everything, we needed the money,' she said.

'Ah,' I said, 'don't worry, I'm sure we can manage.' My mind went back to one of Annie Grant's lectures: what to do if you're somewhere that you haven't got anything. 'Use your initiative, girls.' So while I made the mum and myself a cup of tea, I thought about it. A drawer, yes, a drawer would do. I'm sure I could take the contents out of a drawer, and maybe find something warm that we could pretend was a little mattress. There must be some blanket somewhere. And so it was that this new baby girl, after I'd washed her carefully, was wrapped up and placed in a drawer. It didn't make a bad cot really. The sides of the drawer kept the draughts out and I placed it on the floor next to the low double bed.

In swept Miss White. 'Oh, been a bit busy have we, Nurse Wilkie?' she said, with a smile. She took it all in, in one quick glance. I didn't say anything. Though I'd felt that weight of responsibility in that moment when I realised the baby was coming so quickly, I'd enjoyed it, I'd loved every minute of it and the challenge of finding things for the baby and making the wee ones more comfortable. We found the odd jumper to put on them. We asked their mum about neighbours I could contact to see if one of them would pop in to make some lunch for them.

'Oh,' she said, 'I don't really mix with people round here. They don't like it, you know, that my husband is drinking.'

'Don't you worry,' I said, 'when there's a new baby, people love to help. I'm sure there will be lots of people who will pop in and give you a hand.'

CHAPTER ELEVEN

During all these happy months on the district I was also having tremendous fun with John and enjoying all the things that we liked doing together, without any problems of long distance between Epsom and London or, even worse, Epsom and Edinburgh.

With some friends we had a wonderful skiing holiday in Austria. After we came home the next event was my brother Alexander's wedding to Judy Clark. My two sisters, Mary and Susan, and I were to be bridesmaids. After all the happiness I'd shared with John, I knew in myself that I couldn't go on being around any longer. Our relationship had become much stronger and I needed it to go forward. John had always been open and honest about the fact that he had no intention of getting married or settling down in his twenties, and so I didn't have any expectations, although in my heart that was what I was hoping for. I felt that if our relationship wasn't to be more than it was, I'd have to go away. Quite a long, long way away, in fact, and in my mind I'd even considered Australia, somewhere where I knew the people and having finished my nursing training, I thought, well, I could get a job there. So inside I was sad, although outwardly happy with all that was going on.

Alexander's fiancée Judy and her family lived in Epsom and I helped her with the preparations for the wedding. John had said to me that it would be nice if we could have dinner out one evening before my parents and sisters came down from Scotland and I became totally swept into wedding plans, and that was to be on the Tuesday evening. I was expecting John at about 7 p.m., but 7 p.m. came and went, and 7.30 p.m. also passed by. It must have been nearly 8 p.m. when the doorbell rang, and there stood John in his old mac and the hat he was rather fond of wearing, absolutely soaked. He'd left the car at the end of the drive. He looked bedraggled and tired, and I said, 'Are you all right?' He seemed awfully quiet.

'I'm all right,' he said, 'are you ready?'

So I shouted goodbye to everyone in the house, and off we went in his little green car with the roof firmly on. Well, we were tootling along, and John said, 'I hope you don't mind, but we're going to take Aunty Babs some eggs from my mother on the way.'

'Oh,' I said, 'that's just fine.' I was very fond of his Uncle Donnie who was married to Babs and always enjoyed going to their house.

John still seemed unusually quiet. I suppose my chatter does tend to make up for the two of us, but after a little while I was looking out of the window and thought, this is a very strange way, no, we've gone too far. I said, 'John, I think we're almost in Sutton, we've passed Burden Lane, we're not near Babs and Donnie.'

He pulled the car to a screeching halt and in a distracted sort of way said, 'Oh, how stupid of me, I am being so stupid.'

I said, 'Are you all right?'

'I'm fine,' he said.

Well, he didn't seem like himself at all. However we turned round and eventually arrived at his uncle's home and we stayed and had a rather large gin and tonic. We might even have had two, I can't remember. Then off we went again in the car.

It only took five minutes to reach the restaurant on the Epsom Downs where we were to have dinner. I was enjoying the atmosphere of the restaurant and my dinner, but John was not himself and before I had finished my main course, he said, 'Well, are you ready? I think we ought to go now.'

'But John, I've not finished,' I said, thinking, it's all so strange, I couldn't understand it. I said, 'All right, if you feel we must,' but thought, a peculiar evening out, this: John came late, went the wrong way and now suddenly wants us to leave! He must be feeling poorly, he did look pale.

We got back into John's car and he drove us up along the Downs, where we could see all the lights below and away into the distance. He stopped the car and we were just sitting there silently. Suddenly John spoke, and said, 'Will you marry me, Angela?'

I'd heard the words, but no, I thought, it couldn't have been. I was speechless. The next words I heard were the same, and still no reply from myself. I truly didn't believe it because although I'd been wanting it so much, I'd told myself that he wasn't ever going to ask me. And then he said, 'Are you listening, Angela, are you listening to what I'm saying?'

This somehow jolted me into making a reaction. So the third time he asked me I was just absolutely thrilled. I felt choked saying the yes bit, I was choked with happiness, absolute happiness. I couldn't believe it.

We spoke then about John talking to my father. I knew Daddy was coming down with the family on the Thursday, and John had a night class that evening after work. I suggested that maybe John could speak to Dad back at their hotel. We thought that would be best and somehow I would try and keep quiet about it all until then. But when John took me back to the Clarks' house I wanted to wake them all up and tell them my news.

My family arrived on Thursday afternoon and to my dismay, I heard Mrs Clark kindly inviting them to return to the house and have dinner after the wedding rehearsal, rather than go back to the hotel. This meant of course that all my plans for John meeting Daddy were completely up the creek and I had no way of contacting John to tell him. We all came out of the house after tea, me bursting with the news that I wanted to tell my family, and not knowing how I was going to get Daddy back to the hotel. We got into the car with myself and two sisters sitting in the back, Mum and Dad in the front, and as Daddy drove very straight through the open gate, I just blurted out that John and I had got engaged on Tuesday night. Well, Mary and Susan shouted and screamed with delight and my poor father nearly drove into the gate post. Everyone was full of questions, when was this, and how about that, and I was trying to explain that John was going to be at their hotel at 9 p.m., and I said I was sorry that John hadn't spoken to Daddy first, but it didn't seem to matter.

Then suddenly it was Saturday, and Judy and Alexander's wedding. We talked about the fact that it was very important that our sudden engagement was not spoken of at the wedding because we didn't want to take away from Alexander and Judy's day. The service was lovely, simple and personal. Many friends from my family's side had come a long way from Scotland, and some even happened to be over from Australia. Since the Dobbies and the Clarks had been friendly for such a long time, there were many of John's family and friends at the wedding also.

During the reception my father came across to John and me and said that he and Mum were going to speak quietly to one or two people and invite them for a drink after the reception. 'We won't say what it's about; they will just think it's because we've come from the north and have not had a lot of time to talk to them at the reception.' John and I were truly expecting about a dozen people, but when we went in, the room was crowded. We just mixed in with everybody and were chatting generally when suddenly my father said he would like to say a few words and he announced the exciting news of our engagement. Well, it took the whole party by storm. It was indeed a fantastic surprise. Nobody had realised what the party was for. A lovely way for our engagement to be announced.

Over the weekend, amidst all the happiness, I had a lot to work out. Before our skiing holiday I had received a letter from The Middlesex Hospital offering me the position of Ward Sister on Queen Alex. But I knew that if I were to take it, I would be committing myself for at least two years in the position. That was clearly understood. As I have mentioned, I had been in a lot of turmoil, thinking that I needed to get away, that I couldn't stay near where I could be seeing John. I couldn't handle it. Now, even with our engagement, it was still not right to take up the position. I thought, there's no way that I could run a house in Surrey and be a Ward Sister for a unit like that. I believe the commitment to be enormous. I also believe it is a large commitment to run your own home, and when you're first married I just don't think the two things go together. Many people feel that very dated; I don't mind if they do think that. I personally think that a position as a Ward Sister demands more than a hundred per cent of anyone in it, and equally marriage and running one's home and setting up home requires the same, and you can't be in two places at once.

So that left me with the decision to turn down the position which I had always wanted. But I didn't feel sad about that now. I was swept up in the happiness of our engagement and looking forward to being married. I would look for a post more locally around Epsom where we were going to look for a house. In fact that was what happened. I found an advertisement in the *Lady* for a private maternity case in May, outside Farnham. I contacted the people and had to go down for an interview.

They seemed very nice. They had one little boy of two already. I asked her to give me a clear indication of what my duties would be, and she said 'Well, I'm going to breastfeed but you will be in charge of the baby and myself in terms of meals and everything that the baby and I need. I'm also going to have an *au pair* girl to look after my little boy, and I do have a Spanish lady who comes in two days a week to do the cleaning, so your responsibilities will just be entirely to do with the baby and myself.' It all seemed, I thought, very satisfactory. I did ask her about the nights, and she said that she would have the baby in beside her and her husband. She asked me if I drove and I said, yes I did. 'Oh, that might be useful because we are a bit away from the station here.' I didn't think much about that at the time. I was looking forward to the job.

After six weeks in Scotland I flew south to have a weekend with John whom I hadn't seen since our engagement. I wanted to be looking my best and had my hair done, my nails manicured and even had them painted. I flew to Heathrow, then I took a bus to the London terminal but there, I heard over the Tannoy, 'Calling Miss Wilkie, urgently calling Miss Wilkie.' I thought, oh dear, whatever can it be. But in a moment I realised, the baby, it would be arriving early. Indeed it was. The family had frantically called Edinburgh only to be told that I had left and would be arriving in London, and they just caught me. So instead of taking the train to Epsom, I had to take the train to Farnham, painted nails, posh hairdo, smart clothes, the lot. I arrived at their house in a taxi. The doctor was halfway through delivering the baby. He gave me a withering look, obviously thinking I'd not be much use dressed up as I was. However the delivery was an easy one and the doctor left immediately afterwards, and suddenly I was in charge. I didn't mind that at all, but I was totally unprepared and very disappointed that I wasn't having the weekend with John.

Later in the day the lady said to me, 'Oh I've changed my mind about the baby; I want his cot to be in your room, Angela, it'll be less tiring for me. When he cries, you just bring him through.' And I thought, oh no, I'm going to have broken nights as well, but there was nothing I could say. I was in the job and I was going to have to get on with it. It was quickly apparent that the *au pair* girl could hardly boil an egg. The lady who was meant to come and clean the house twice a week did come but her idea of cleaning and mine did not match up. So if the household were to have anything to eat it was going to have to be me who did the cooking and in terms of hygiene, the house seemed a positive health hazard: that was going to have to be my responsibility as well. The last straw was that the father of the household came back late from the city every evening and expected his dinner to be placed in front of him at 10 p.m.

A week and a half into my time there, I was utterly exhausted, and unfortunately I caught a nasty chest cold from the wee two-year-old. Immediately my concern was for the baby and mother, so I started to wear a mask so I wouldn't pass the germs on. I do remember having a day off on the second weekend, but I was feeling awful. I'd hardly ever had a bad cold and certainly not one that made me cough like that. John kindly came down in his car and took me out for the day. I was not at my best. I liked the job, I truly did. I didn't mind that it was hard work, and I didn't in fact mind that I had to do all the extra things that I've mentioned. But I was increasingly over-tired which rather spoilt it.

While I was there I was again thinking ahead, and I heard of a position which was going at the Epsom Cottage Hospital for a Ward Sister, which I thought would be just the thing. I understood that with such a position I could live in which would solve the problem of accommodation. So I arranged to go for an interview at the end of my time with the family. I was delighted with the Cottage Hospital and the fact that it was small. The Matron, Miss Allan, seemed excellent and since the position was vacant I could start right away. I said I'd be delighted, thank you.

So I came, not in very good health, to work at the Epsom Cottage Hospital. I was given the women's ward where the patients were in for both surgical and medical reasons. The doctors, mostly GPs and some Consultants, I found very helpful, but on my second day there, when the lunches came from the kitchen in a big heated trolley, one of the Sisters from the other wards who had worked at the hospital for years announced that she would be serving lunch that day. I felt more than a little surprised and, inside, not pleased at all. I thought, well, I know I'm new here, but I would have thought at least I could serve lunch for my own patients on my own ward. However, I thought, it's early days, I'd better keep quiet today. The lunches were given out, to my horror, in rather large portions, far too much for many people, and almost impossible for some to contemplate eating, especially those who had no appetite anyway. I decided to make a stand about this. It was not popular, but I did insist that I should serve the patients on my ward their meals in future. I'd been trained to the fact that meals were an integral part of treatment for all patients, and needed careful handling, backed up by a knowledge of the individual patient's needs.

My off duty was spent mostly out with John and house-hunting. I still had this dreadful cough. It would not go away. Nobody seemed to think it was infectious any more, it was just a sort of leftover from a nasty cold. The fact was that I did still feel quite tired, but of course, truth to say, I was burning the candle at both ends. We were out a lot and sometimes late, and I worked hard so it was no wonder that I felt tired most of the time.

Another incident on the ward which highlights something else in nursing that I think is important was to do with the cleaning. I had noticed and been much concerned that the bathrooms and toilets of my ward were not being cleaned properly. A delicate matter, indeed. One weekend when things weren't too busy I decided to have a crack at them myself, so that on the Monday morning I followed the cleaning lady into the bathroom, making sure that there were no patients at all to hear our conversation. I decided to say the few words I needed to right there.

'Oh,' she said, 'have you got somebody new doing the job?'

'No,' I replied, 'I had some spare time over the weekend and I cleaned them all myself.'

'Oh, why did you do that?' she said. 'What has been wrong with them?'

'Well,' I continued, 'the fact is that your position here, looking after the bathrooms and toilets and helping the ward to be clean generally is a very important job.'

She looked at me, totally surprised. 'Oh, do you think so?' she said 'Why is that?'

Obviously no one had ever made her feel that. So I went on to explain, 'Unless these bathrooms and toilets are kept spotless we will not be able to control the rate of infection. All the work that the doctors can achieve, whether it's in the theatre, or by medication, and all the things that the nurses are doing for the patients, all that work will be wasted and the patients will become more ill rather than getting better.'

Silence from this lady. I could see she was thinking my words over.

'Oh,' she said, 'I see what you mean, but nobody has ever explained that to me before.'

'Well, I can assure you that you are an important person and a very important member of the team. You're just as important as the doctor and the nurses, and the patients need you to do your job the very best that you can.'

A great beaming smile appeared over her face. It was as if she couldn't wait to get on with her job so I left her to it.

CHAPTER TWELVE

I had been at Epsom Cottage Hospital about seven weeks. It was extremely hot summer weather and I was off duty in my nurses' accommodation. I remember itching the shin of my right leg, thinking, oh, I've been bitten by something, but as I scratched it, I thought, oh, how peculiar, it feels sort of odd. I didn't think much about it. I thought I had probably got a bite in the hospital garden that afternoon, when I'd been sunbathing. Then a couple of days later, I happened to touch the same part of my leg again, and thought, that's most peculiar, it feels a bit numb, and each day after that for a week, I kept touching my right leg, and to my horror, I thought, it's not just one little part of my leg, it's from the knee downwards that it feels different. I couldn't think of anything that it could be and it wasn't bothering me, but at the same time my nursing training told me that I should speak to a doctor. At the end of the week I made an appointment to see the staff doctor.

The day came for the appointment and I went in. He asked me one or two questions about my general health and I said, 'Well, I'm always very well indeed, but I have to admit I have had a cough which has hung on since I did a private midwifery case.'

'Oh,' he said, 'pretty strenuous job was that?'

'Oh, not really,' I said, 'it was flat out for three weeks and I did feel a bit run down at the end, and I suppose I have been feeling a bit tired since but it's the cough and maybe I'm not sleeping as much as I usually do, and I admit I have been going out a lot and I love the work here. I'm fine really but it's this stupid thing on my leg.'

He said, 'What do you mean, on your leg?'

So out came the pins (they keep them behind their lapels). He started to prick my leg and then said, 'Well, I'm not at all surprised. I can imagine you're working extremely hard on the ward here, and as there are some heavy cases which require lifting I'm quite sure you're thoroughly overdoing it, Sister.' He said, 'You're having a good time when you're off duty, working flat out when you're on duty, and, if you'll pardon my saying so, you came to us in a run down condition.'

'I suppose you're right,' I said. 'But I don't feel poorly.'

'No,' he said, 'but probably what's happened is that you have trapped a nerve when lifting somebody and this has caused a bit of numbness in your leg.'

I thought, well, I don't remember lifting anybody badly. We'd been taught how to lift and we were very careful how we did it.

He continued, 'I'll get you an appointment with the orthopaedic consultant here and I'm quite sure that she can find out what the problem is and clear it up for you, no doubt make you take things a little easier. These things usually resolve in a few weeks' time.'

So I thanked him very much and went back on duty, and just carried on.

A few more days went by and I was phoned up to be told that the orthopaedic consultant could fit me in the following day. It all seemed a lot of fuss about a small part of my leg. However, somehow when you start something, you're swept along with it. So I duly arrived for the orthopaedic appointment and the lady seemed rather cool, I thought, but I suppose I was – well, I wasn't worried, but I couldn't tie it up somehow. I didn't feel I'd lifted anyone badly and there wasn't any pain where I might have trapped a nerve. I answered her questions, and she examined me thoroughly, remaining silent as she did so.

Then to my absolute amazement she said, 'I'm not the right kind of doctor at all. What you need, Sister Wilkie, is a neurologist.'

'A neurologist,' I said, 'but, what for?'

'Well, it's nothing orthopaedic,' she said, 'I couldn't say what it is. I mean, I don't know, necessarily, but I think you ought to go and see a neurologist.'

At that precise moment, I thought, there has to be more to this than I realise, and I thought, although it's only a small part of my leg, I've seen a GP and now an orthopaedic consultant, and am heading for a neurologist. The moment this orthopaedic consultant said that, I thought, right, there's only one place I would like to see a neurologist and that would be Dr Michael Kremer at The Middlesex Hospital in London where I trained. I came out of that consulting room, feeling worried and suddenly admitting much more to myself how tired I felt. But there was work to do, and I went back on duty. It was hot, and that makes you more tired, and my mind was not a hundred per cent on my work. I was pleased that I could choose the neurologist. It gave me, well, just a little crack of confidence, the fact that I would be going to a hospital that I knew and to a consultant whom I knew slightly. I had to wait a couple of weeks to get my out-patient appointment to see Dr Kremer and during that time I continued working but I was feeling more and more tired. I still had my cough. It hadn't eased at all. But much worse than that, this stupid leg of mine seemed to be more affected, now from the knee down to my foot, I thought. It's awful, you keep touching something like that, to sort of test it every now and again and then you wish you hadn't because you realise that it's slightly more affected than say two or three days before. Very unsettling.

The day came for me to go up to London and as I walked from the hospital to the station I felt extremely tired. The sun beat down on me, I felt cooked and the train was stuffy. I felt lonely, really. I thought, don't be stupid, Angela. Dr Kremer will sort me out. Then, of course, after the train journey, there was the tube from Waterloo to Goudge Street and then another walk to the out-patient department. I found myself sitting on a seat in the out-patient department waiting. I must say, it's a very different feeling being the patient. The time goes so slowly. I was exhausted. Eventually my name was called and I went in to see Doctor Kremer. What a charming gentleman he was. He had a firm handshake and kind eyes, and he made me feel totally at ease as he asked me to sit down. He asked me several questions and I went through much of what I've mentioned about being overtired, having a bad chest cold, coughing a lot and now this stupid – well, I called it stupid because I didn't understand it – bit of bother with my leg.

I said, 'It's just from my right knee downwards, but in fact, of course, a couple of weeks ago, it was a tiny part, and now it seems to be so much more.'

'Hmm,' he said, 'yes, these things.'

'But,' I said, 'what sort of things, what is it?'

'Well,' he said, 'what we have to do now are some investigations. We can't ever find out in a moment what's happening, and it's totally unwise to hazard a guess. We'll have to ask you to come into the hospital.'

Come in? This was getting worse by the minute. 'Oh no,' I said, 'couldn't I have them as an out-patient?'

'No,' he said, 'I think it would be much better if you come in to the nurses' ward, Princess Alice.'

'Oh, I worked there for a bit.'

'Well, that's fine, you'll know the unit. It won't do you any harm at all, Sister Wilkie, to have a little rest for a start. We could clear up that cough and find out what's the matter with the leg. Now it might be one or two days before I can get you a bed but I'd like you to come in as soon as possible.'

'But,' I said, 'I'm working, I have a Ward Sister's job down in Epsom.'

'Yes,' he said, 'I know that, the orthopaedic consultant told me. They'll understand. Anyone can require to be off duty for a few days.'

'How long would it be, do you think?'

'Oh, well, I wouldn't like to commit myself, but it wouldn't be for long,' but he said at the same time we ought to keep an open mind, and take one day at a time. He was extremely kind, but firm. 'Right,' he said, 'I'll have my secretary contact you as soon as we have a bed available.'

I stood up and thanked him and left the room. It all seemed quite unreal. Suddenly I'm not the nurse, the Staff Nurse, the midwife or the Ward Sister, but the patient on the other side of the fence. I did feel extraordinary.

The day was still hot. That glaring dusty heat of London hit me as I left the out-patient department and went, not in a daze, but not myself, back to the hospital, and up to my little room. They'd given me the day off to go up to London for this appointment. I just flopped on the bed and before I knew it, well, I'd woken up from having had quite a sleep. I phoned John and told him how I'd got on and that I had to go into hospital and I couldn't understand what was going on, but we would just have to take one day at a time. I kept saying, 'I feel fine in myself, I feel fine, it's just whatever is the matter with my leg, we'll have to find out.' I explained to Matron that I would be requiring time off to go into hospital.

'Quite understand, Sister, don't worry about it at all, we'll have somebody cover the ward for you while you're away.'

I carried on working the few more days that it took to receive the phone call to go into the nurses' ward as a patient.

Such a strange feeling being in the hospital where I had trained. There were endless numbers of doctors who came round and stuck pins in me, and did all the different tests. Then they x-rayed all of me, muttered about my chest and also my teeth. Nothing seemed to tie up in my thinking at all, and I remember one of the doctors saying, 'Don't try and work it out, let the boss do that. Dr Kremer will be to see you the day after tomorrow and he'll have the results of the tests. In the meantime he's asked me to say that he'd like you to have complete bedrest. You may only get up to go to the loo and to have a bath.' And I thought, well, this is overdoing it. To lie in bed all day! I mean, the day before I was tearing up and down as a Ward Sister, rather tired, it's true, with that stupid cough, but now the change, being stuck in bed. However, you don't argue as a patient, you do as you are told.

My bed was at the far end of the ward from the door, in the corner by the window overlooking the front of the hospital. I could see right down Berners Street. They let me walk to the bathroom and the loo, they were literally four yards from my bed so I wasn't exactly going to get any exercise. Lying in bed is not very comfortable. It makes you very sore. It's very boring and lonely. It gives you far too much time to think, to worry, to try to work things out, which of course is not at all wise. The nurses were excellent, as indeed were all the staff. John was marvellous in visiting me. Nearly every evening he came from work.

Dr Kremer came on his rounds and he said, 'Well, we've done the tests and we've got you in the right place.'

And I said, 'Well, what is it?'

He said, 'You know those dental x-rays? We think they show that you've got some infection in one of your teeth which has travelled down your spine a bit and is affecting a nerve going to your leg.'

'Really,' I said. It sounded extraordinary to me. But then, you don't argue, not with a consultant neurologist, especially one of his reputation.

He continued, 'This means a lot more rest, complete rest. We'll have that tooth taken out properly, under an anaesthetic, we'll clear up the infections but I'm afraid things to do with nerves are a bit slow.'

'Oh.' Another short remark from myself. 'Thank you,' I said. Funny remark that, how we say thank you when we don't quite know what else to say. Dr Kremer, his registrar, houseman and the students moved away from my bed, and I just sat there thinking, well, this is going to be so boring, I can't bear it, I can't believe it.

At the end of three weeks they said I'd be able to go home. I thought, go home, I don't want to go home to Scotland. But of course I realised that there was no way I could go straight back on duty and live in the Cottage Hospital. Dr Kremer came on his own one day, sat down, and said, 'Angela, I don't think it's wise to be carrying on with the nursing position you have at the moment. It's extremely demanding and we don't want this problem to recur. I have to advise you that you ought to consider standing down.'

I couldn't believe it. Being a Ward Sister was what I'd always wanted to do. I had that choked feeling inside. I didn't have any words to express it. It was more than sadness, it was almost like an anger of upset, churning around inside me. Yet I knew in my heart that I would have to do as I was told. I said to him that my mother and father were going to come down. 'Ah yes,' he said, 'that's excellent, you can go back home with them.' Again, I felt so quiet. There was an inevitability about it.

The following day my parents arrived and it was wonderful to see them. They both looked tired and strained, but I thought, well, it can't be very nice having your daughter as a patient, and I was enthusiastic about Dr Kremer but told them that I should have to stop my nursing while I had a good rest at home. They sort of nodded their heads and seemed very quiet. After a short visit, they stood up and said they'd be back later and we'd talk about the plans to go home. I didn't want to go to Scotland, I wanted to stay down near John. By the time Mum and Dad returned later that day, I was more myself. The nurses had let me walk about a bit to get my legs going and the thought of being out of hospital definitely cheered me up. The following afternoon Mum and Dad took me the short distance down to Berner's Hotel where they were staying.

John appeared at the hotel after work, and Mum and Dad very kindly suggested that maybe the two of us would like to go out and have dinner on our own. I thought this was great, and there were plenty of small restaurants very near by. I mean, you only have to cross over Oxford Street and you're into Soho. Mum and Dad were worried, would that be too far? I said, 'No, no, that's fine.' Of course you try and brazen it out that you're much stronger than you're really feeling, but I wasn't too bad, and I didn't think it would be too far. I thought, wonderful, how generous of Mum and Dad to think of us wanting to have the evening to ourselves. We walked down the road, across Oxford Street, found this tiny restaurant, and went in. There was a red and white gingham tablecloth and a candle in a wine bottle with dribbled candle wax down it on each table. Only a few people were there, besides ourselves. The waiter came, we ordered a drink and he gave us the menu. I wasn't hungry, not at all really. When you've been in hospital you don't get up much appetite. It was so lovely to be out. It sounds as if I'd been in prison. Everyone had been excellent and more than kind but it was wonderful to be just ordinary again, and not a patient.

John was very quiet, but straight away, before we had time to talk about anything, he said, 'I've got something I've got to say, Angela, and I think I should say it now.'

And I said, 'Oh, what is that?'

He said, 'It's something awfully hard.' He looked so white and pale, and I thought, it's probably just the lighting in here. He said, 'Your Mum and Dad have been talking to Dr Kremer.'

'Oh yes,' I said, 'I thought they'd probably have a chat with him because he mentioned that to me; it seemed a good idea and puts them in the picture, and lets them understand what's been going on. It's always a good thing, that.'

'Yes, but there's a bit more to it, Angela.'

'Well,' I said, 'they've told me.'

He said, 'Yes, I know they've told you about this infection in your spine and it'll take a while.'

I said, 'Yes, that's right.'

'Well,' he said, the fact is that Dr Kremer has told your parents that you have multiple sclerosis, and your parents have told me today that this is what it is. I've been to see Dr Kremer today myself, and he has said that this is what it is.'

My silence, just complete. No words at all. The end of everything. All I could think of was the absolute end of everything. There was no way that we could or should get married. It would be totally unfair to John. I could see now why Dr Kremer had been trying to tell me gently that I ought to be giving up my nursing career. John so bravely spoke these awful words, which he'd been given the job of doing – dreadful that. I do believe that was the doctor's responsibility. As John saw my reaction, he became paler than white, if that's possible. It was simply horrendous, in this small restaurant, with our world in smithereens. Completely shattered by a few sentences. For one moment I thought, help, John's going to faint, the whole thing was too much for both of us.

I couldn't understand. Why would they have given him the job of telling me? It seemed so wrong, that. I learned later that when Dr Kremer told my parents, they had immediately asked if he had told me, and he had said, oh no, he didn't think I needed telling, with all my training, that I would have guessed by now. You don't guess. I'm not stupid, but you don't guess, you don't diagnose yourself. Although it had been my first ward, neurology, it hadn't even once in all the weeks crossed my mind that it was anything like MS. People might find that unbelievable or naive, but it's the truth. So the shock was absolute, and too much to cope with. Somehow we helped each other make our way back to the Berner's Hotel, where Mum and Dad picked up the pieces, and helped us as best they could. I had to say goodbye to John and face going home and cancelling the wedding.

CHAPTER THIRTEEN

Human beings have a bad record of underestimating people and in my misery and stress I was totally underestimating John, only because I didn't want to put him through what I thought could be years of difficulty. In no time at all he was on the phone reassuring me, insisting of course we would be married. Plans had been made for us to be married in St Cuthbert's in Edinburgh in March. Plenty of time to feel stronger and better. In any case, there was lots to do to get ready. I continued to protest that it shouldn't be, it wouldn't be right, but he said, 'I've had a long chat to Dr Kremer. Something like MS, there can be very long periods of remission. Some people just have one little bout like you've had now, and many many years with no trouble at all. It's true, others have it differently, but nobody, no specialist at all, can tell us how it might be.'

I couldn't believe it. What wonderful words to hear but I kept trying to cancel any excitement. Gradually, as John insisted, I came to believe it and by now was feeling absolutely fine. My legs were stronger; the numbness seemed to have disappeared. In fact, I felt a bit of a fraud, almost as if I had been in a bad dream, and come out the other end of a dark tunnel. My head was telling me though that I hadn't imagined it. But now the hope was there, more than a hope, the reality that John believed it was okay if we got married, and I could look forward to all the happiness again.

In September Dr Kremer gave me full marks on my checkup and he said, 'Now, I don't need to see you for at least six months. Go away and be happy.' I remember telling him that we were getting married and he wished us all the best. He didn't say, oh you shouldn't, or you mustn't, or what a bad idea. So I returned to Scotland and the plans had been made, as I've mentioned, for our wedding to be in March.

But one night John phoned and he said, 'This is ridiculous, you're up there in Scotland and I'm down here in England; why don't we just change our plans?' He said, 'Angela, choose any Saturday you like in January.'

Well, I laughed, because when we'd first talked about getting married we'd both said definitely that January would be a hideous month for a wedding.

We wouldn't have any money, not that we had much anyway, in fact, practically nothing, not saved up, I mean. But it made sense, that we could be together. Why wait until March? There was absolutely no point in waiting. I wasn't going to be able to go back to my nursing career. Somehow we could look for a house and sort that side of things out. So we decided on 12th January. Well, consternation! Poor Mum and Dad, they couldn't believe it. 'But we have everything booked for March. Angela, you don't want to be married right after New Year, and January. People who might come a distance for your wedding certainly won't want to come in January. There'll be ice and snow. Oh no, please reconsider.' But John and I were adamant. We'd chosen the day, 12th January.

It's amazing what can be rearranged. Mum and Dad were wonderful. John started to look around for a house. I went down several times. Eventually we found a small semi-detached house up near Epsom Downs, 69 Parsonsfield Road. The next problem, of course, was to afford it. I didn't have money saved up. I'd spent the money Grandpa gave me for my twenty-first on contact lenses which I was struggling to find helpful. However, I did have a little bit of money which an uncle had given me, an aunt of John's very kindly lent us a little, and also my mama. Somehow we got together the money. I think it was £3,600 which nowadays sounds ridiculous, but to us then it was a lot of money.

The weeks were spinning past, and I'd chosen my bridesmaids: my best friend Audrey from my schooldays as my chief bridesmaid, my two sisters Mary and Susan, my cousin Carol, and my great friend Diana. Five bridesmaids. What a lot it seems now. And the colour. Flamed coral, I thought. We'll have a warm colour with it being January and everyone sure it was going to snow. Well, even if it does, it won't matter. I was feeling wonderful. I was sure that it would be a wonderful day, and I wasn't in the least bit nervous but when the day came, if I'm honest, when I went to get my hair done in town, I had butterflies in my tummy which were not helped when I arrived home to find the house in a turmoil and Mum saying, 'You must eat something, Angela.' But I didn't fancy anything. The bridesmaids had arrived and their dresses were all hanging up ready for them and a lady was coming from the business, Wilkie's, to get me dressed. I remember going up that lovely staircase, in No. 21, and into the large L-shaped drawing room. As I slipped into my dress and one of the staff from Wilkie's kindly zipped me up, I remember that moment feeling absolutely happy and confident and calm, with no nerves at all. We had lots of photographs taken in the drawing room and then they all swept off leaving Daddy and me on our own. Then I realised it was Daddy who was nervous.

We arrived at St Cuthbert's. Someone had kindly put a red carpet down on

Our wedding day

L-R: Alec Wilkie, Madge Dobbie; John; Angela; Ida Wilkie; Donald Mackay (John's uncle)

the steps up to the front door of the church. Nobody thinks of this, I suppose, but by the time all the guests had gone up this beautiful red carpet into the church, it was covered in wet snow and mud. My dress had a train. I didn't know until later, but evidently the train on my dress was absolutely black.

The minister, Dr Leonard Small, was standing at the end of the aisle with John and our best man Sam Stevenson. I remember holding John's hand. Since Leonard Small knew me especially well, he made our service extremely personal. Our vows to cherish each other in sickness and in health were the same as others say but more poignant for John and me that day. I sensed that all our family and friends thought that too. It was very moving and as we went in to sign the register in the vestry, I do remember asking John if he had a hankie, thinking, gulp. But it was only a tear. After one night in Gullane, down the coast from Edinburgh, we travelled on the overnight sleeper to London as we planned to stay a night in John's mother's house while she stayed on in Scotland for two weeks.

At this stage I was still totally in ignorance of where we were going on our honeymoon. John was insisting that it was to be a surprise. I knew it had to be somewhere abroad because we needed our passports. In those days the minister had to sign your passport and give it to you once you were married. I don't think John told me until we were on the train to London that we were going to Paris.

We got down to his mama's house in Epsom where the first shock hit us. As John opened the front door, we could both see something was not right. That winter was so severe and unfortunately his mother had turned the heating off and every radiator in the Dobbies' house had burst, with the frozen water inside expanding. There was ice all over the walls, the floor, the furniture, in every room, absolutely everywhere. There we stood aghast in our posh wedding clothes, ready to go on our honeymoon. John immediately tried to phone round and get a plumber to help him, but of course they were all out and they were all busy and it quickly became apparent that there wasn't going to be any help from anybody. One of them kindly said he would lend John some tools which would enable him to unscrew every radiator and carry it out into the garden, because we knew that the minute the weather eased up a bit, all that ice would thaw, and his mother's house would be flooded. So all that day and well into the Monday night before we flew to Paris was taken up entirely with John unscrewing radiators, and me chip, chipping away at the ice off the walls and the floors or wherever I could, so that it wouldn't melt eventually and cause more damage. All in posh clothes, because the rest were packed to go.

And then the last straw somehow was when we were tired and cold and hungry, and I remember going into the kitchen thinking a hot drink was certainly what we were needing. John had gone up into the loft to check the tanks and various things like that, and suddenly I looked up and there, through the ceiling, not far from where I was standing, was this water drip, dripping through. As I turned round in my tiredness and anxiety at the whole situation, I slipped on the floor, and I remember calling out to John and he came down from the loft and he said, 'Oh my goodness, what have you done?' Well, of course, in a flash I thought, oh probably I've done my back in or broken a leg or something. You think of something dramatically dreadful. In fact I hadn't hurt myself. Basically I was frightened and tired and cold, we both were. John kindly got me tucked up in bed and kept saying, 'Don't worry, we'll soon sort it out and it will all be well in the morning.' I couldn't wait for the morning when we could leave and go down to Lydd airport and fly to Paris away from all of this.

We stayed in a small hotel in the Montmartre district, not far from where you go up the steps to the Sacré Coeur. I was relieved to find that the clothes I'd packed were fine for Paris. They were casual, but I was intrigued to know why John had said also to bring something really smart. John told me that Angus Cameron, a longstanding friend of his family, had said that as a wedding present he would pay for us to go to the Lido and have dinner and watch the floor show, a truly fabulous night. I specially enjoyed climbing the steps to the Sacré Coeur where we watched the artists at work in the little square there, and we had a trip down the Seine, a visit to the Louvre and a night at the Opera. The days were cold but the skies were blue and the winter sunshine stayed with us all week. Paris was quiet which made an extra delight for us.

CHAPTER FOURTEEN

More excitement ahead, because we were going into our own house, 69 Parsonsfield Road. But while we'd been in Paris, the snow had been falling steadily in England and when we got back it was about a foot deep in our small garden. The roads were covered in thick ice. Immediately John had to give me a few special lessons on driving in hazardous conditions because I wasn't used to it. The snow didn't last for just a few days or a week. It lasted on and off for nearly two months. It was an exceptionally severe winter, 1963, and because we were high up the snow lasted longer. I soon got used to driving the car though in those conditions because I took John every morning down to the train and then I had the car during the day and would collect him in the evening.

The better weather came at last and we were having a very sociable happy time these first few months of our marriage, going out and entertaining friends at home. We were lucky to have the car and to have our own home, utterly spoilt to have it so well furnished with all the presents we'd been given. And I was feeling great. I felt marvellous. I didn't feel as if I'd had any bother the summer before. Because I was so happy and busy I wasn't even missing my nursing. Each evening I would sit in the car at the station and wait for John to come off the London train.

One particular evening, I was sitting there and I couldn't help but notice all the billboards and I thought, that looks a bit odd, and I remember shutting one eye and keeping the other open and then vice versa, and I thought, most peculiar that, I must have something in my eye. But I didn't think anything special about it, and John arrived off the train and he drove home. I didn't mention anything about my eye or even think about it until the following evening, when in exactly the same situation I found myself doing the same with my eyes. To my concern, I thought, one eye is definitely slightly blurred, it's not the same as the other one. My heart sank. We'd only been married five months. Please could it not be trouble coming at us, no, please not.

I had to tell John, of course, and then I had to ring Dr Kremer's secretary and ask if I could speak to him sometime. He was excellent about that. He'd always said that if I was worried I could speak to him on the telephone. Pretty special that, to be able to do that with a London consultant. Totally spoilt. 'Well,' he said, 'you're due for a checkup anyway, why don't you just pop up and see me and we'll take it from there. Don't worry about it.' That's easier said than done.

Dr Kremer said, 'Well, I'm afraid you have got a bit of a problem in one eye. Just try and take things a bit easier, and rest up a bit. I know it's boring, but it's truly worth it, Angela.'

I nodded and quietly said, 'Yes, I know.'

He was such a delightful gentleman, firm but very kind. So I went home with the news to John and we both tried hard not to let it worry us, get us down. In fact my eye seemed to improve quite quickly.

Now the summer was moving on, to June, and the news from home was not good. Daddy had been quite unwell, and was taken into the Nuffield Private Nursing Home. He was having pains in his chest and they thought that there was something wrong with his heart. They ran all the tests through, but they couldn't find anything at all wrong with his heart. He was much improved by the rest and the plan was that the family including Daddy were all going to congregate together up at Ardoinig on the shore of Loch Tay. John and I planned to join the family at this lovely place. It was such an opportunity to have a holiday in Scotland and see all the family.

I could hear the telephone ringing. It woke me up. It must have been between eleven and twelve. Halfway down the stairs my mind told me that this phone was ringing to tell me something dreadful about Daddy. I just knew it, and as I picked up the phone and heard Alexander's voice, he didn't even have to tell me. The night staff had gone in to settle our father for the night and he was so looking forward to going home and to the holiday we were all going to share at his favourite place. Evidently after the nurse had settled him down for the night and gone in to the next patient, our father had rung his bell, but by the time she'd rushed back into his room, he'd died.

Alexander was being marvellous and strong and I was saying at my end that we'd be right up on the train. And when I got home, poor Mum, it was all too much. I was very conscious that being the eldest I must support Mum as much as possible and must not allow myself to break down and I must let Mum be able to lean on me and help her in every way possible. And also, my sisters were only young. I mean, Susie was only fourteen and Mary just sixteen; in fact she'd just had her birthday a month before. And there was Alexander, only twenty-four.

It was decided to carry on as usual about the holiday. I know, a strange thing to do, but in our terrible sadness, nobody seemed to think that that wouldn't be the right thing to do. It was absolutely awful. It was the wrong thing to do. Everything, the very loch itself, the house, the big stone we called the Fat Man where Daddy used to fish from, the boats, the people, everything was a reminder of him. It was totally unwise but somehow we were there and we had to carry on with it. Mum was doing her best and we all tried to support her. But it was so hard. Later, when I returned to our own home with John, it was only then that the full impact of it all hit me, and I felt absolutely devastated. Thank goodness I'd managed to hold on, mostly, when I was with Mum and the girls. Eventually I got myself together. John was marvellous. We kept busy. It just didn't seem possible. Daddy was so young to have died like that.

After all of this, which of course was a huge stress, I felt my wretched leg again a little bit numb. I thought, this is not a good summer. So back again I went to see Dr Kremer and this time he said, 'Well, I really think this time, Angela, you ought to come in for a few days. You've had a tremendous lot of stress and I think rest here with us is what you need.' Back again, then, to the Princess Alice Ward at The Middlesex. Everyone was so marvellous and kind. I truly felt a fraud, sitting up in my posh trousseau nightie with people kindly coming to visit me. It used to be like a party in the evening. John would come from Shell, and sometimes other friends at the same time. I didn't feel ill at all but I'd been firmly told that I must rest as much as possible. So I did.

And then after a couple of days Dr Kremer came in with his usual entourage. He came right up and sat on the edge of the bed and he said, 'Now, we've been having a little chat and we were wondering . . . we want to put a proposition to you. There is some thinking that we could give you intramuscularly a form of hydrocortisone called ACTH. It would mean having a daily injection of this, but this would be very experimental. It wouldn't be for very long; we're not sure at all what, if any, reaction you might have to it. We won't give you too much because we'd just like to do it as a trial. Now, we'd like you to think about it, and talk to John about it, and then you could let me know.'

Well, straight away I said, 'Well, if you think it would be helpful, surely we should do it?' I said, 'I'll speak to John tonight.'

John agreed with me that because Dr Kremer thought it would be a good idea, we would want to give it a try.

So a couple of days later a staff nurse came to explain about the injection. 'The solution is a bit thick and so we'll have to use a large needle. I'll do it as quickly as possible.' She was excellent, thank goodness, but it was rather sore. However, you can get used to anything, I thought, if it's going to be a help. Well, after two or three days, I felt tremendous, very perky and the numbness had gone from my leg. I was saying, 'Oh it's wonderful, oh, I'm fine,' but everyone else was saying, 'Hang on a minute, Angela, it's far too soon to judge if it's really the answer.' They were doing constant blood tests and all sorts of other tests on me and I just couldn't wait to be allowed home. They said, 'You can in fact go home in a few days' time and have this injection from the district nurse.' Each day I was dramatically stronger, even my walking was improved. I felt on top of the world and going home was such a thrill. The district nurse came every morning and gave me this intramuscular injection of ACTH. Dr Kremer explained that it would be cut down fairly quickly after I went home because of their concern about the side effects. At this point I felt marvellous and all seemed well.

I had an appointment to go back and see Dr Kremer three months later but long before that time had passed, if I were honest with myself, I knew that the numbness was back again. Such disappointment. It hadn't lasted long, it hadn't lasted at all. All my euphoria and happiness was for nothing. Back to Dr Kremer.

'I'm sorry,' he said, 'we've boosted your hopes. But,' he said, 'to be quite honest, your reaction to this injection was a surprise to us. We didn't know what to expect but your system responded dramatically. Because of our concern about the side effects we don't want to give you too much. It's rather unclear how these injections work in certain situations. We will have to feel our way slowly. Obviously, when you were on the injections all was well but your system is reverting back to the problem without them, and we can't give you the injections all the time.'

Difficult, I thought, so difficult. But somehow Dr Kremer made it bearable to hear the difficult words. He said, 'Don't worry, we'll try the injections again. Now we know how your system responds, we'll vary it a little and this time give you less and see if that would still have the same good result.'

I agreed and so we started another course of the injections, and again I went home. The same routine, with the district nurse coming. I felt quite weak when I went home, but each day I was stronger, and then I was absolutely bouncing full of energy.

One evening, we thought we'd go and have a few holes of golf. I had no idea whether I'd be up to it or not. There's something debilitating about being in hospital. John suggested that I take my putter and number 4 iron. He said, 'We'll just play one hole and see how you get on and if you feel that's fine, we'll play as many or as few holes as you feel up to.' I shall always remember that evening. I wasn't trying to hit the ball hard. I just swung the club easily and gently but to my astonishment the ball went such a distance. And it proves the point about letting the club do the work. We played several holes. It was wonderful to be on the golf course again; it boosted my morale tremendously.

We went through two years of that, me being on the injections, feeling wonderful, coming off them, and each time the problem recurring. Although it's true that the time in between each episode became longer, then Dr Kremer decided no more injections. He said, 'We'll see how things go from month to month.' I was fine, but not a hundred per cent. I could still drive, go dancing, play golf, indeed I could do everything, but of course there was always that nagging tick of worry which only surfaced sometimes, but for both of us it was there.

Our summer holidays were mostly golfing ones, which suited both of us. We would just take off in the car – it was lasting very well – and we were off. We stayed in small bed and breakfast places and had dinner out somewhere, golfed wherever we chose, with a bit of time at the beach if it was nice enough.

We also went north to Scotland, of course. Mum had moved house round the corner from No. 21, still in the same street in Edinburgh, to a beautiful flat with a fabulous garden. I remember feeling swamped by my large family. I know it was only out of concern, but they kept wanting me to sit down and rest and were constantly saying, 'Oh don't do that, Angela, you'd better not,' and I was feeling suffocated. But John spoke to them and explained there was no need for me to rest all the time, in fact, quite the opposite. It was so important to allow me to carry on as usual.

Carrying on as usual was tiring me and we were seriously thinking about moving into a bungalow. It wasn't sensible to be living in a house that had stairs. Everything however seemed so expensive. We did see a house that seemed perfect to us in Byfleet, had our offer accepted and then suffered the pain of being gazumped.

Springtime came and John went with the Shell hockey team to play in Amsterdam at Easter. My mum said she'd come down and stay while he was away. On Good Friday, while reading the many particular notices coming in from estate agents, I came across the details of a bungalow in West Horsley. It sounded absolutely wonderful and I said to Mum, 'Why don't we drive down and have a look at it?' We found the address quite easily. I stopped the car. We couldn't believe it. It was totally flat, wonderfully easy for me if my walking was a problem. But my most vivid first impression was of masses of tulips, wallflowers and forget-me-nots in the flat front garden. It was stunning to look at and a dream to enjoy the perfume.

We both felt it would be unsuitable to disturb people but I couldn't resist ringing the bell to see if I could make an appointment. A lady answered the door, tall and with a welcoming smile, and I explained how we'd had the particulars about the house and although I didn't want to intrude maybe we could make an appointment and come back when it was suitable. She kindly said, 'Why don't you come in now?'

I said, 'Well, my mother's in the car; would it be all right if she came in with me?'

'By all means,' she said, 'please do, we'd be delighted to show you both round.'

More perfumes from the garden pervaded the air as the French doors were open from the sitting room to a huge back garden. I fell in love with Shortlands. It was just perfect for us and I could see immediately that living on one level would be a great help, less tiring. Immediately I thought, over this holiday weekend, Easter, masses of people might look round and it will be sold before John even sees it. I voiced my concern to this delightful couple.

'Oh, no, I wouldn't worry, I don't think anything will happen over Easter,' they said. 'Why don't you bring your husband when he comes home? Just give us a ring and we'd be delighted to show you both round again.'

As I drove back to Parsonsfield Road I was so excited, but reality was also entering my mind. The price. 'Mum, what's the price? I can't bear it, I didn't even look.'

'Well,' she said, 'Angela, it's £11,000.'

'Well, that's it,' I said. 'We shouldn't have even looked at it.'

'Well, you never know, people do come down in price. You don't necessarily have to offer what they're asking.'

'Oh,' I said, 'Mum, England's quite different, it doesn't work out like that down here. People can gazump you,' and I immediately felt despondent about it all.

Mum and I had a happy weekend but all I wanted was for Monday evening to come. I was picking up John at the airport. I thought, I can't wait until Tuesday to show him the house, we'll have to make it Monday. The men came off the flight and you can imagine the last thing any one of them wanted to do was to go and look at a house. But my enthusiasm for Shortlands spilled over and John sensed it was something not to miss, so he agreed that I should drive him down to see it. I could see that John was enthusiastic about it, but I could sense also that he was being realistic immediately, rather than later, on the price. We thanked the couple, but John made it quite clear. He said, 'We would like to buy your house but quite honestly we can't afford £11,000. We would like to make an offer and we will make it the very best offer we can, because for lots of reasons it would be a special house for us.'

We drove home, and I thought, well there's no way we can raise that kind of money. I mean, it's just not on. But Mum was wonderful, and she said, 'I'll help you out. I could lend you some and you can pay me back on a proper transaction with the bank. And maybe you'll get more for Parsonsfield Road than you think.'

So John got in touch with the lawyers and estate agents and the best that we could do was to offer £9,500 and that was pushing it. Well, we didn't hear anything so we thought definitely we'd missed it. And then about ten days later we had a phone call from the gentleman who owned Shortlands and he said would we like to go down for coffee that Sunday morning? We thought, gracious, what a weird invitation. But at the same time it was exciting because we thought it must give us a little ray of hope. We drove down and as we went through into the sitting room the lady offered coffee, which I took. Meanwhile her husband said, 'I think we men folk will just take a walk round the garden.' I took a look at John's face and could see he was thinking, wonder how this will go. Well, I sat there, drinking coffee and making conversation with this charming lady, but all the time making every effort not to talk about the house. I knew I'd know by John's face when they returned in from the garden. They seemed ages out there. We could see them going round and around. Eventually, in they came, and I could tell immediately that they were going to let us have it. I was ecstatic. We were so thrilled and they were charming about it and said the reason they were selling it to us for that money was they felt that we would be happy in their home where they themselves had been happy for nineteen years.

Not only was I thrilled about our new home but I quickly realised the difference living on one level made. I was much less tired. I revelled in the garden, enjoying the challenge of keeping it as beautiful as had its former owners. For quite a few months before moving to West Horsley I had been excited because Dr Kremer had at last said that since I'd been off steroids for quite some time, it would be all right to try and start a family. I so wanted a baby and he assured me not to worry about it, just to go ahead. But I was disappointed that after six months I wasn't pregnant.

I was resolved to go and speak to our GP about it, feeling that he would be bound to think this was some young woman who was being over-anxious. But I misjudged him completely. He said, 'Oh you're quite right; if you've been trying for about six months now I think we should check you out and see if you have any problems.'

I said that we were going on holiday the following week.

'Oh well,' he said, 'in that case take a thermometer with you.'

Well, of course, I did know, having done my midwifery, that your temperature goes up in the morning when you're ovulating.

'Good gracious, that's going a bit over the top,' I said, 'taking my temperature every morning.'

'No,' he said, 'it's quite a simple thing to do. Try it.' I thought, definitely

I'm not going to mention this to John.

Fortunately, the first morning of our holiday I woke up early, so I popped the thermometer in my mouth and turned my head away in case John were to wake up. I had my pen and paper beside the bed and as I wrote down what it was I thought, this is definitely contrived and overdoing it. I didn't fancy the idea but thought, you just never know. Well, the next morning I did the same. I woke up and popped the thermometer in my mouth but as luck would have it, I dozed off and the next thing I knew was John shaking my shoulder saying, 'What on earth is the matter? Why are you taking your temperature?' Well, of course we had such a laugh about it. I mean it really must have looked ridiculous, lying there with a thermometer in my mouth, fast asleep. And it was then I told him about all the doctor had said. In fact, it turned out that I did ovulate at slightly unusual timing. I returned to see the GP, pretty sure by all the signs that I was expecting a baby.

It was decided that I should have the baby at The Middlesex Hospital and then Dr Kremer could also have me under his beady eye. During the entire pregnancy I felt absolutely wonderful, and in no way did it make me too tired or poorly, or give me trouble with my legs. In fact, I felt sparklingly well the whole time.

As so often happens in people's lives, everything comes at once. We'd no sooner learned about the baby when one day the telephone rang. It was my brother who, since my father's death, had been carrying a very heavy load as the Managing Director of Wilkie's in Edinburgh. I could just hear John's end of the conversation when Alexander rang but I heard John repeating, 'Come to Edinburgh, join Wilkie's,' and in my heart at that moment, I thought, oh no, I couldn't imagine it. I simply couldn't imagine John going from Shell International to a family retailing business. But John, in his wisdom at the time, could see that it was such an opportunity.

That phone call completely altered the course of our lives. John, naturally, wanted to think about it, and by the time he came off the phone I'd already given myself a lecture which was that such a decision must be John's. After all, it was he who was to be working in a totally different situation, going from the male-orientated world of Shell International to a women's fashion business. It was primarily women's in those days and mostly women in the staff, only a very few men. It came to me as more than a shock, when we talked it over and I realised that John felt he should accept Alexander's offer.

In the autumn John left Shell International and went to work in Bentalls in Kingston where he learned about the totally different world of a retail store.

It was wonderful to be feeling so well and I was enjoying playing golf quite often. John and I had entered a mixed foursome competition one Sunday afternoon. To our delight and surprise we won it. As it happened, that was the very last time I played golf, but as I was expecting the baby and planning our move to Edinburgh I didn't miss it then. There was much to think about and prepare. I was confident that I could look after the baby, having had my nursing and midwifery training, but knew that since my balance was not perfect there were one or two things I needed to sort out. I made a rule, there and then, that I would not walk anywhere carrying the baby. We bought a large carrycot on wheels and I was going to use it to push the baby around both inside and outside.

Then I thought, if I had a large desk, with drawers down one side and a space where I could get my knees under to enable me to sit down, then I would have the baby's things in the drawers, a changing mat on top, and a safe situation for looking after my baby. There was something else I learned to do during those winter months. I learned to sit down to do the ironing. When first I tried it I thought, oh, I can't possibly be doing with this, but of course, there's no such word as can't. My board went to a lower height, I pulled up a chair. It was a fiddle, I felt, to begin with to get the right height, but I got used to it.

Time was passing. Christmas came and went and we still had to sell Shortlands. Although I'd felt fantastic throughout the pregnancy I knew that I would have to go to hospital two weeks before the baby was due. I didn't relish going up to the hospital. I thought it was going to be so boring, remembering my many times as a patient. However, this time I wasn't in the nurses' ward, I was in the maternity unit, in a small room with just two other expectant mums who, like myself, had to have some rest before they went into labour. So that left me in the hospital and John staying at his mama's in Epsom and going to work at Bentalls in Kingston. And still we were looking for somewhere to stay in Edinburgh.

Up north, my mother and my cousin Anthony had been constantly on the lookout for something that would be suitable for us in an area that we fancied. I'd only been in the hospital for four days when we got word from Scotland that Mum had heard of a house, a bungalow, at 20 Barnton Gardens, and my cousin Anthony had come to hear of another one, very similar, at number 26. John decided to fly up and look at both houses, and he would have a choice – extraordinary that. Very exciting. That certainly was a special day for us. He looked at both houses and chose No. 20. Anthony decided that he and wife Alison would buy No. 26. John flew back to London and drove from the airport to his mother's house.

Meanwhile, in The Middlesex Hospital maternity unit our baby had decided to arrive ten days early. I was in the first stage of labour at midnight and by that time John had just arrived back at his mother's home in Epsom.

The midwife said, 'You know, Mrs Dobbie, if your husband would like to be here when the baby arrives, he'll need to come now.'

I replied, 'Oh, he's been in Edinburgh today, he'll only just be getting back to Epsom,' but I thought how sad I'd be if he wasn't with me. However, Sister was great and phoned John's mother's house to ask John if he could manage to come up to London as quickly as possible. So having been to Edinburgh and bought a house, and returned to Epsom, Surrey, he drove up to London – some day that!

Well, when he arrived, I was having frequent contractions and had had an injection, which I know makes one a bit woozy, and I remember John walking into the little room I was in, on the labour suite, and I said, 'Why are you wearing my dressing gown?' I think John thought, what on earth is the matter with her? She's talking absolute rubbish. But of course, as the midwife explained to him, it was just the effect of the injection.

I couldn't believe how quick everything was. Our wonderful baby girl arrived safely in six hours from start to finish. We were both so thrilled. And what a surprise, she had lovely pale golden hair. Everyone commented, no one had seen a baby with hair like that in London. And the day after I had Clare Dr Kremer came with his team to see me and our baby. One of the young doctors stepped forward and said, 'Don't you think, sir, this baby looks jaundiced?' I felt for that young man so much because Dr Kremer turned round and said sharply, 'Don't be so stupid, young man, this baby is a Scottish baby and she has pale auburn hair. Most unusual, I grant you, but certainly she's not jaundiced.' That poor young man, I thought, he'd never forget that.

I was learning how to look after my own baby but, although a fully trained nurse and midwife, I was often fumbling and not managing. Certainly when it came to the stage of bathing Clare for the first time, I thought, I'm definitely going to drown her. My head was telling me, don't be stupid, Angela, you've bathed hundreds of babies, but it is different when you're the mum. It's totally different.

CHAPTER FIFTEEN

They kept me in hospital about six days, anxious that I should rest as much as possible. And then what bliss it was to be able to go home. My mum had flown down from Edinburgh and was kindly going to run the house for me and help me for the first little while until I got into a routine. All the preparations that I'd made for the nursery, and which I'd thought of ahead, suddenly became excellent working and practical arrangements. I didn't feel at all that there was ever a moment when I could have harmed Clare if my legs were not a hundred per cent. The house, with only one step at the front door, the level path up to it and the flat cul-de-sac we were in, all made it easy for me to take Clare out.

When the time came that we should move up to Edinburgh, Clare was about seven weeks old. I flew up with Clare, and John drove up. John met us at the airport and everything was happening at once. The large removal van was also at the gate and John was worried that I wouldn't like the house. We came through the gate. On my right was a beautiful terrace, and behind it a long white bungalow with a red pantiled roof, a sunny house because I saw all the main rooms were facing south onto a huge garden. I could see it would be more happiness for me because I loved gardens so. Quickly I could see why John was concerned. I don't think the house had been loved very much. There were huge scratches on all the doors – I think a dog had maybe been shut in the rooms – and the whole house certainly needed a spring clean. That could soon be accomplished. The doors were wide and the front and back doors had only one step. John had thought about that most carefully. It had three bedrooms, one of which we made into a nursery for Clare, with the same arrangements that I had had down south.

It was a busy time for both of us, with John learning more about Wilkie's and myself settling in as a new mum. We knew lots of people, at least I knew lots of people from years before when I'd lived in Edinburgh. We made new friends from all walks of life.

John got into the Royal Burgess golf club after we came to Edinburgh. Down in England we'd been used to the golf club being a country club. A sociable place to be. But here, to our horror, we learned, when John became a member, that children were not allowed. I thought, oh, what a shame; I had been looking forward to the occasional lunch out, taking our baby with us. I couldn't believe it. I knew it was male members only at the club but I didn't see why that had to preclude women in a social way. Women were allowed to sit in the hall for a drink before dinner or lunch, and children were not allowed at all. John asked the captain and council, has this been a long-standing rule? Would they consider changing their mind? He said, our baby's nine months old. We can't say that she's an angel but we feel sure that she could come here without causing any bother. It was explained that a mother a few years before had changed her baby in the bar. Well, women weren't even allowed in the bar so I don't know how that came about, but because of that this sanction was made. The council pondered over it and decided maybe they'd give it another try providing we could assure them our baby could behave. So this particular Sunday we arrived, somewhat nervously, hoping Clare was going to behave. We needn't have worried. They had a high chair ready for her at the table. Clare sat happily in it and in no time at all many members of the club came up to us and said, 'Oh, what a darling, and what a pleasure to see a wee one in the golf club again.' A happy lunch out for us and a new rule allowing complete families to come to the golf club, which of course is how it should be.

Before I'd left London, Dr Kremer at The Middlesex Hospital had assured me that he knew a neurologist in Edinburgh – Dr Clifford Mawdsley – and he was going to write and ask him if he would look after me when we arrived in Edinburgh, and thereafter. It helped a lot to feel that I was being passed on, as it were, in a personal way. It brings me to the point that it makes an enormous difference to believe in the specialist who's looking after you, to come to know him as a friend as well as a doctor. I found Dr Mawdsley to be a young, very brilliant neurologist who was frank and open, and immediately I felt at ease with him. If he said anything I didn't quite understand I could easily ask him to explain in a different way. We would talk about all sorts of matters, be they the news of the day, politics, and even holidays, indeed about anything other than that which I'd gone to see him about. It was his way, I felt, looking back on it, of finding out how I was coping with my situation.

I was managing fine and keeping well. It's true I did get tired a little. I stuck to my rule of only having Clare in the carrycot on wheels if I was going round the house or anywhere that required taking her from A to B. Our car was a great help and I didn't have any problem getting her carrycot into the back seat.

We found Edinburgh a very sociable place. There was never any problem about someone to look after Clare if I wanted to go on a special shopping trip or outing, and I would take my turn of having friends' children. The house lent itself to entertaining. The rooms were a good size but not too big, and the garden, absolutely wonderful. Such a pretty house with the red pantile roof and a large lawn, which in those days had huge herbaceous borders running up either side of it, and behind one herbaceous border was a large vegetable patch. It was all rather too much, that, the vegetables I mean. I had brought all my dahlia tubers up with me from Horsley and I managed to plant all one hundred of them sitting on one of those little low woven stools because I couldn't stand or bend over for long, my balance being a problem at this time. Being one-third of an acre the garden did seem overwhelming at times because John was more interested in playing golf. I was no longer able to play and trying hard to accept the fact.

There were various challenges ahead of me, mostly to do with looking after Clare and it was still easy for me when she graduated to a pushchair but once on her feet I'd have to find a way that was different. She was fast and I was slow.

In fact, as a two-year-old, Clare did have many escapades. Between the kitchen and the dining room we put up one of those stair gates so that she could see me in the kitchen but at the same time be safe and have plenty of space to play.

With Clare aged 2

One day I could hear her crying and I shouted out, 'Where are you, Clare, come to Mummy now.' She knew to come to me, that it was difficult for me to get to her. But I could tell the wailing was coming from the end of the garden and it was becoming louder and louder. I thought, somehow or another I must get there. And when I eventually got there, my balance not good, there she was, stuck with one knee in between the fencing. She of course had been trying to climb over. There was no way she was going to go forwards or backwards or over the top.

There was another day she completely floored me. John was at work and Clare was safely in the garden, I thought, as we kept both our main gates wired up. Suddenly the back door bell rang, and there on the step was a stern, extremely well-dressed lady, clutching Clare's little hand firmly, and saying, 'I believe Clare is your daughter.'

I felt absolutely horrified. I said, 'What do you mean, where was she? I thought she was in the garden.'

'She was certainly not in your garden, Mrs Dobbie. I know that's your name, your daughter told me. At least you've taught her her name and proper address.'

You can imagine I was feeling such a stupid and useless mother. But I said, 'Where was she?'

'Well, she must have gone over the gate since I had to untie it to get in,' she said. 'She must have gone down along that main road, crossed over and gone into Safeway, because that was where I met her, Mrs Dobbie.'

I was absolutely mortified and thanked the lady profusely for bringing Clare home.

That September, when Clare was two-and-a-half, we went to have tea one day with a friend of mine, Jane Steven, and her little boy Angus, together with another friend of Jane's with her small child of about three. The following morning Jane rang me up and said, 'Angela, I don't suppose for a minute this will affect you, but I have to tell you that the little one who was here with my friend has developed German measles, and I'm just ringing to tell you in case, by any sheer chance, you might be expecting a baby.' Well, in fact, it so happened that I had only just learned that we were going to have another baby. I think I was about eight weeks, which is the most dangerous time, of course. 'But,' I told Jane, 'I'm quite sure I had German measles when I was ten.'

However, it did seem wise to ring our doctor and ask him what he thought. 'Well,' he said, 'it's too risky to take a chance. Come straight down and I'll take a blood test and see if you have any immunity.'

I did that, and the next morning Dr Strachan was on the phone early, saying, 'Get down here as fast as you can. You can't have had German measles, you haven't a shred of immunity, Angela, and the risk to the baby is at its worst.'

I went down to the surgery and was horrified to see the size of syringe necessary to have a gammaglobulin injection. Anyway, it was definitely worth it to be assured there would be no risk at all to the baby.

John and I were delighted that Clare wasn't going to be an only one. I was most fortunate that Clare, very active as she was and into all sorts of things, still happily had a wee rest after her lunch, which allowed me the chance of doing the same. That was more than fortunate because, of course, like anyone expecting a baby, I did need a bit of rest.

I was going to have the baby at the Western General in Edinburgh. Having managed with Clare in the way that I've told you, with my desk as a changing table and all the things to hand, I felt I knew what to do and wasn't concerned about how I'd manage. But of course it would be different this time, having a little one running around and a baby as well. Dr Mawdsley was seeing me at regular intervals and, as I've said, I was keeping well but it's true that my walking was not so good. I think I must have been about five months pregnant when I went to see him at the hospital, and as I stood at the door of his room I remember thinking, it seems a long way from the door to his desk. I thought, I hope I'm going to make it. I could feel that his beady eyes were upon me. I did make it, but he knew me far too well not to see and understand that it had been an effort. When I sat down in front of him he looked me straight in the eye and said, 'Well, Angela, which is it going to be? Are you going to lose this baby, or are you going to use a walking stick?'

Initial silence from myself, but only for a moment. And then I said, 'Of course, I'll use a stick.'

He was absolutely right in the way he said it. Only he could have persuaded me to use one. In my anxiety not to fall I soon overcame my embarrassment about using a stick to lean on. It made the most enormous difference not going from piece of furniture to piece of furniture, or from an open door into a room which could seem like an absolute chasm. Very disconcerting, and these sorts of feelings are all made worse if you feel that other people are watching. Now I know of course people were not watching to see how I was managing, but because of my embarrassment I felt that they were. A difficult emotion, that, to cope with, but you just have to get used to it. As always John encouraged me and made light of these things. We carried on our lives as if my legs were just fine. It's true I did have wobbly legs but we did all the things everybody else could do and somehow, in a way, appreciated much which others took for granted.

At Christmas time we were at a party, given by great friends of ours, J. and

Jen Burnet, and I met a man whom I'd met all those years ago when I was doing my midwifery at the Simpson. He had been a student doing his obstretics there. He looked me up and down and said, pointing to my large bump, 'Where are you going to have that, Angela?'

I said, 'At the Western under Mr Clarke.'

'Oh,' he said, 'that's interesting. I'm his senior registrar. Would you like me to look after you and keep an eye on you, and maybe deliver the baby?'

I thought, amazing, that would be simply wonderful to have somebody that I knew and to see one person consistently. And so it was that Alan Brown, after that, always saw me when I went to the clinic, which made all the difference.

The winter months sped on, and the baby was due at the beginning of April. The doctors insisted that I arranged for somebody to come and help me for the first three months. They said, 'You need another pair of hands, and you must have your sleep at night.' Again I was advised not to feed the baby myself. It would be more convenient to get somebody in to help, so I interviewed several people and had the good fortune to meet the most delightful young lady, Ava Herrman, and it was all arranged for her to come as an au pair.

I went into the Western a couple of weeks before the baby was due and was shown into a room for two, where there was another young woman who had serious diabetes and had been there for many weeks on bed rest. I was fortunate to be allowed up but she was made to lie in bed all the time.

The days dragged on, and John and I had not chosen a girl's name. We'd kept the names of Stephen and Christopher from when we'd had Clare. I thought, this is ridiculous, there must be a name that we both like. When I had about ten days to go my friend in the room received a letter from her niece which she proceeded to read out. Amongst the pages she came to the name Lisa, and I said, 'Oh, I do like that. Oh definitely, that's wonderful, I never thought of it, oh, I must ask John.' And when I tried it out on him that evening he immediately said, 'Oh yes, I like it fine.' Well, we'd no sooner been talking about names, when in walked the doctors who said, 'We've been talking, Angela, and we think we ought to start you off tomorrow.'

In fact, I beat them to it. I didn't have to have a drip. That evening after visiting I suddenly started in labour and John, who was going to be with me, was by then having dinner with great friends of ours who were also friends of Alan, the registrar. I remember distinctly being wheeled along to the labour suite, thinking, John's not going to make it, I'm going to have this baby so quickly. I couldn't believe it. On the one hand, good to be so quick, but on the other hand, I wanted John to be with me. Lying in the labour suite there, and with the pains coming every two or three minutes, I could hear Alan as he went to the phone. I could hear him say, 'Oh, hello there, Bobby.' He said nothing about the baby coming. To my horror he started talking about golf and when he and Bobby were going to play their next match, what time, what day, and where. I was trying to do my breathing and thinking, John will never get here, when suddenly I heard Alan say, 'Oh, by the way, Bobby, it's really John I need. Would you tell him to get up here immediately, the baby's coming any minute.'

Anyway, John arrived, and I had such an easy time. I'd only been in labour for an hour and a half from start to finish and there we had another lovely baby girl. The minute they said that, I turned round immediately to see John's face, thinking, oh dear, is he going to be disappointed that it's not a boy? But not at all, he didn't seem to mind. And I couldn't explain, in myself, the tremendous happiness that I felt that the baby was another girl. I hadn't knowingly wanted another girl but I felt absolutely thrilled, and so there we were.

Before I had Lisa the doctors had said, 'You know, two babies are plenty, we wouldn't want you to have any more.' We both agreed that it would be unwise. Therefore the doctors had suggested that I have a sterilisation, only a little op which you can have done twenty-four hours after you have been delivered of a baby. I thought nothing of this at all, because everyone said it was a very minor operation. I would have an anaesthetic but it would be very quick and I would hardly know I'd had it. The following day the anaesthetist came and wrote out the form, the pre-med, which didn't mean anything to me. I went to the theatre and the first thing I can remember is waking up on a stretcher in the large recovery room that they have for people who need an eye kept on them before going back to the ward. In an instant I was terrified. I was lying on my back on this trolley, which wasn't comfortable but that was the least of the problems. The fact was that I couldn't get my breath. I couldn't understand it, and try as I might to call anyone my voice seemed awfully little as if nothing was coming out. There were all these people around me, lying on stretchers, like being in a morgue. It was a very frightening experience and, of course, I suppose it wasn't very long before one of the nurses came to me and got me on my side and I managed to breathe more easily. They quite quickly took me back to the ward where I was popped into bed, and I felt just awful.

And when I was lying there, having a bit of a doze, in walked our minister, Dr Small. Well, he got the most enormous shock. Instead of seeing a happy mum with a new-born baby sitting up and smiles all round, there I was, ashen-faced, lying flat out in my bed. He couldn't think what on earth was the matter. He came up to my bedside. He said, 'Angela, whatever has happened?'

I said, 'Oh, it's all right really, I've just had a little op today and I've reacted badly to something, but I'll be all right.'

He sat down beside me. It was so fortunate that it was him, a wonderful man, sensitive and quiet. Had it been anybody else, I don't know how I would have coped because I felt dreadful and totally not in control. At the same time I didn't really understand why I felt so poorly when I'd felt wonderful the night before when Lisa was born.

Later we learned that the pre-medication that they'd given me was an intramuscular injection of valium, and this is something which does not suit my system. It had made my intercostal muscles so relaxed that they weren't functioning properly, and when I came round I was toiling to get my breath. However, I soon bounced back. It didn't seem long before it was time to get my clothes on for going home. I do remember that day. Shame on me, I had to wear my red maternity dress because I couldn't fit into anything else. Something dreadful about that, when you can't wear something more normal. However, I made quite sure as soon as I got home that I did find something that I could squeeze myself into. Anything was better than to remain in maternity clothes.

I had made it absolutely clear when I first met Ava that the main reason I required her help for three months was to enable me to have as much rest as possible. She would be the one to give Lisa her bottle during the night, apart from her two nights off, when I would have Lisa in our room. So I had plenty of sleep and lots of help, and felt wonderful.

CHAPTER SIXTEEN

It's true that at this time, April 1971, my walking wasn't marvellous and as I've mentioned I was using a walking stick. We planned to go to the Colne Houses Hotel at Cromer in Norfolk for our holiday because of the excellent facilities and nanny help provided, to enable mums and dads to have some time in the day to themselves. Our room had french doors to the garden, making it easy for me.

Being able to cope on my own with help from the nannies in the hotel enabled John to go and play golf, which unfortunately I couldn't share with him. It's extremely important, that. I was the one who had these stupid legs and I was determined that I was always going to run my life and organise things the very best I could, in order that John would have his life affected as little as possible. I believe that trying always to carry on as usual was much the best way. I didn't feel I was a disabled person with wobbly legs. I didn't think like that and I didn't want to think like that. Now I'm sure, on reflection, that people seeing me walking with difficulty and using a stick would be thinking, oh dear, poor lady, fancy two children and all that, but in myself I didn't feel like that. Not at all. So it didn't weigh me down, depress me or upset me. John was fantastic and we had two lovely daughters. I'd always been and still was a practical person, so that was a benefit too. Ideas would come at odd times, which helped me in practical ways. You could call it learning by experience. Yes, I learned many ways of doing things differently in order that things would appear as if they were just the same.

An important thing which I had to learn again, was to drive. I was still driving our car but we had to face the fact that I should consider having a hand-controlled car. I was told you could apply for a Government mini with hand controls, and such a thing would be funded by the DHSS. I thought that would be fantastic. Somebody put me in touch with the Vehicle Centre in Edinburgh where I learned that not only would they fund me a hand-controlled mini but also they would pay for me to have driving lessons. Well, this was certainly something else. I'd learned to drive in the ordinary way when I'd been in Edinburgh doing my midwifery but these lessons were an absolute nightmare.

It was with great difficulty that I learned to drive with hand controls. It wasn't the road sense and all that, it was all so much to do with my hands. There was the steering wheel which had attached to the right of it an acceleration lever, a brake lever and a clutch. The acceleration one you brought towards you and the brake one you pushed away. Then there were, of course, the ordinary gears to be manipulated with my left hand while I depressed the clutch lever with my right. And you may well ask which hand, if any, was on the steering wheel? Well, you start off with both hands on the steering wheel and learn to work these three levers on the right, keeping your thumb on the steering wheel. And if you're changing gear, you choose very carefully where you're doing that and how you're doing that. I had many many lessons, and I was in tears often. Frankly, I did not think I was going to succeed. But it was so important to me that I felt, I've got to make it, I've just got to. My lessons always had to be with the instructor because we didn't personally have a hand-controlled car, so it was quite expensive, and most generous, I thought, of the Government to fund it.

Eventually the dreaded day dawned when I was to go out to the test centre, and I particularly remember having a lesson just before, as people often do. And while I was driving along, it suddenly started to rain. In a moment I realised I had no idea where the switch was for the windscreen wipers. It was an extremely fortunate incident to happen beforehand because when we went back to the test centre it continued to rain throughout my test. I'm quite sure I could have been failed on just not knowing how to switch on the wipers. The test instructor took me to the top of Corstorphine Hill and there, in the most difficult circumstances, he made me do my three-point turn and hill starts. To my astonishment I passed. I couldn't believe it. It meant so much, and I was most fortunate to receive the blue Government mini with hand controls.

With life wonderfully full and busy as it was for us in these days, with our two girls of four and one-and-a-bit, my new car made all the difference. I wasn't walking as well as I might, even with the help of the walking stick. During that summer Dr Mawdsley said now that I had the children it would be safe to try some more steroids and he'd like to try me out on some dexamethasone tablets, which are a form of steroids. To his surprise, I think, I responded dramatically. I felt wonderful. My walking seemed much improved. My spirits were up and I felt a totally different person, but the trouble, of course, is that you can only have anything like that for a limited time and then you start the usual, reducing the tablets until you stop them altogether. It was very similar to my body's reaction to the injections I'd had all those years before. I saw Dr Mawdsley regularly but was also in hospital several times for rest, physiotherapy and some steroid treatment. Dr Mawdsley would constantly say, 'Try not to get overtired,' looking at me straight in the eye. He knew perfectly well that was sometimes difficult.

He was absolutely right, and our GP, Dr Gibbs, who had newly joined our practice, said, 'Frankly, the thing to do is have somebody come in the afternoons who could take the girls out for a walk to make sure that you do have the rest you need. Then you'll be keeping well and have the energy to enjoy the children and your social life.' At fifteen months Lisa was on her feet and had no intention of having a little rest. Clare had been so excellent in going down for a wee sleep after lunch until she was three, which suited me down to the ground. So I advertised and in response a delightful young lady, Sue, came to help me with the children in the afternoons. It made all the difference, it truly did, as well as having some help with the housework three mornings a week. Dr Mawdsley, as indeed had Dr Kremer, kept impressing upon me that being overtired was the danger, and if I didn't take note of that, I would be likely to become worse in some way.

September came, and it was time for Clare to go to nursery school. She could hardly wait. I knew she'd love it. She was very sociable and enjoyed the company of other children. That first morning when I drove her to nursery school at Murrayfield Gardens I opened the car door for her, out she jumped, and with hardly a backward glance, rushed on in. I had wanted to get out but she said, 'No, Mummy, goodbye.' I sat there feeling unwanted and useless. I drove home feeling utterly miserable and couldn't believe how upset I was. I was hardly in the door when my cousin Alison Petrie phoned up from just along the road. 'I'll be right along,' she said, 'get the kettle on, I'll be right along for coffee.' I wiped my eyes and tried to get myself together. She was along before I knew it. They were only six doors away. 'I know,' she said, 'isn't it ghastly. I felt just the same the first time when Nicola went to school. But they love it so, and it's just today you'll feel like that. And you've got Lisa, and there's so much that you do and enjoy.' It was wonderful to have a friend like that who understood completely how I felt.

It was, as I've mentioned, natural for me to invite people in, to entertain a lot, for the children to have their friends in, and for generally the house to be, not full of people all the time, but to be a busy place with comings and goings, probably a lot more than some households, and particularly more than most people who have a walking problem. I was very fortunate to have all the help at home. Both close family and friends were absolutely marvellous in helping in all sorts of ways, sometimes just popping in, or looking after the children while I had an appointment, or even taking them for a few days if I had to be in hospital. People all these years have been wonderfully supportive to John and me; that has made all the difference in the world to us and we thank them for that.

CHAPTER SEVENTEEN

One evening when John and I were at a party in Polwarth Terrace at our great friends Pam and Ross Flockart's house we met a lot of different people. At this party everyone was standing up and as it wasn't possible for me to do that any more I had to find a chair. A charming couple came up and were speaking to me and I surprised myself by saying that I was thinking it was time I did something to occupy my time when the girls were both at nursery school. We talked about my interests and different things that I'd done and I mentioned my nursing and my interest in people generally. I had no idea who this lady and gentleman were but completely out of the blue the lady, whose name was Ann, said to me, 'Why don't you become a marriage guidance counsellor?'

I said, 'A what? A marriage guidance counsellor? I couldn't possibly, I don't even know what they do. Well, I don't think I'd be at all suitable.'

'Oh, she said, 'I think you would be.'

I still had no idea who she was. Her husband seemed to agree with her. It was all most awkward in that they both seemed to latch onto the idea and stood there in front of me trying to encourage me to think about it. Well, I didn't even want to think about it. I know I was looking forward to having some new interests, but I could hardly think that that would be one of them. They drifted off and spoke to other people and others came and spoke to me and we had some delicious supper made by Pam. Then Ann and her husband came back again before the party finished.

'Well,' they said, 'have you been thinking about it?'

I was trying to explain to them that I didn't think I was at all suitable, and didn't really feel that it was what I wanted, and they in their turn were explaining that it would be most interesting and that you were given an excellent training for it. But they did warn me that there was a difficulty in the beginning in that only a very few of those who applied would be selected as suitable. Applicants would be invited to a selection weekend, during which people would assess whether applicants would be a suitable candidate for the training. It did sound quite intriguing, I must admit, I began to think that. However, the party was coming to a close and, as I said goodbye to them, I hadn't committed myself in any way at all, and they I think realised that maybe they'd been pressing me a lot throughout the party. John and I went home a little later and I remember thinking quite a lot, but not doing anything about it. But I wasn't altogether surprised when a few days later I received a lot of information about marriage guidance counselling, with the application forms and a wee note from this delightful couple encouraging me to think seriously about it, and to take the first step to see how I got on. I remembered that the night of the party they had explained that you could just do, for instance, one morning a week which, of course, would have suited me well. I thought, that would be fine. That would mean I needn't be out of the house when the girls were at home. Three hours was the minimum time that you could do. That would just fit in, I thought. I could drop them off at school and go on into town.

So it seemed a definite possibility that I could take up such an interest, supposing I was suitable, at no inconvenience to the family. I decided to fill in the forms and send them away and was delighted to receive a letter inviting me to one of the selection weekends. Inside this there was a lot more information about the sort of thing that would take place. It sounded pretty daunting, I thought. It was to be in October. Suddenly I was intrigued and looking forward to this test to see if I would be suitable for such a training and for such work. I couldn't imagine it, not at all really, despite a lot of my experiences in nursing. However, when I arrived on Friday evening I realised that others there were equally unsure. Some had seen an advertisement in the paper and had applied through that, and in different ways people had come to apply for the selection weekend. It was explained at the beginning that it would be a matter of putting us through a number of tests and interviews with psychiatrists, and putting us in situations where we would be role playing. I hadn't done anything like that before. And the thought of having an interview with a psychiatrist: I didn't look forward to that.

The first thing they made us do was sit in a very large circle. I think there were about eighteen of us, men and women, of different ages and from totally different backgrounds, most interesting that. One of them was called Morag Eakin. We seemed to pal up right at the beginning. It was great to have a friend so quickly when it was all so strange. Suddenly there we were in this large circle of people with the lady in charge saying she was going to go round the circle and give each person a marriage problem and we were to say, off the top of our head, how we would deal with it, or what we would advise. I do remember that I wasn't first. I was very glad about that. But strangely enough it was fascinating. And when it came to my turn it didn't seem all that difficult to say, in a straight-out practical way, what I thought at the time. I felt completely relaxed about the weekend. I thought, if I'm meant to be a counsellor they'll pick me, and if I'm not, they won't. I didn't have any ideas of what they were, indeed, looking for. Looking round at the enormous differences in age and skills of people there, there didn't seem to be a set pattern for a particular type of person who you could say would be suitable as a marriage guidance counsellor.

When it came to being seen by the psychiatrist I did feel nervous and uneasy, I don't know why. As I sat down he looked at a piece of paper, obviously with a few details about me on it. When he looked up he challenged me, eyeball to eyeball. 'Why didn't you go to university?' he said. I thought, what an extraordinary question from somebody who didn't even know me.

I replied, 'Because I didn't want to, I was keen to do my nursing. I managed to get into a London hospital and I enjoyed my training very much indeed.'

He kept going on about the university, and about it being a waste that I hadn't gone. He worried over it like a dog over a bone. He wouldn't let it go, he went on and on. I thought to myself, he's trying to make me angry. In fact, I did feel angry. I thought, I'm dashed if I'm going to let him know that. So I calmly answered each of his questions and stuck to what I felt, stood my ground, and eventually he changed the subject to other things. I didn't like him, I didn't like him at all, but then no doubt he was doing his job and trying to find in me things which maybe I didn't like myself or I didn't recognise or want to recognise. They are clever people, psychiatrists and, of course, it is extremely important that someone like that should test all candidates. I came out of there and I felt absolutely exhausted. There were quite a lot of people milling around outside the door and I remember seeing the next candidate going in. I thought, I'm glad my session is over. It so happened that I was quite near the door of that room when that person came out, a lady in her thirties, I think. She was absolutely in tears.

'Oh,' she said, 'it was awful, wasn't it awful?'

'Oh,' I said, 'poor you.'

She said, 'I kept trying to think what he wanted me to say.'

I thought to myself, poor lady, disaster, just the very thing they try to trip you up with.

The weekend was also a happy social one, giving us an opportunity to get to know other candidates. There's nothing like being in at the deep end together to get to know people quickly. The following day was similar but slightly more difficult in the tasks they gave us and in the type of role-playing that we had to do. What I particularly remember about that day was the very final thing. We sat in a room in which they'd put desks of some sort, and there was a screen at the end. We were told that we would be seeing a series of pictures, one at a time. The picture would be flashed up on the screen and we would have thirty seconds to look at the picture and then we would have five minutes to write a story that that picture prompted in our minds. The paper and pencil were in front of us. Daunting, I thought. There was no time to think any more. The first picture flashed up on the screen. It was an experience which I've never had before or since. I found myself writing on the paper most extraordinary stories. Whatever came into my head I put it down. There was no time to do anything else. Five minutes seemed to go in a flash. There were six pictures altogether and then, even worse than that, we were told that we would have to write about ourselves for five minutes. Altogether a most interesting test, there was no doubt about it, with so little time to think what you might say for each story. I felt it was a form of brainwashing. You had to put down what was in your mind, otherwise you'd end up with nothing by the time you edited this or that out. Fascinating really. I'm sure they must find out a lot about people in such an exercise. But I found it unpleasant to write about myself. You don't know what to put in or leave out. However it all came to a conclusion and I said goodbye to my new friends, wondering who on earth would be chosen.

There were to be, I think, three selection weekends and only a few candidates would be chosen from each weekend. I went home thinking, well, I've enjoyed it enormously, it intrigued me and interested me. I enjoyed the mix of people and I felt that maybe it was something that I could do. I didn't feel any pressure about whether I would be chosen or not. I thought as I did at the beginning. If they think I'll be any good at it, fine, but otherwise I'll think of something else. But I have to admit, having said that, when many weeks later I received a letter inviting me to do the training to be a counsellor I was thrilled. That started a most interesting time for me, going to training weekends, and then starting with one or two clients, one morning a week for three hours. That pleased me as it fitted in with the children. But, of course, it wasn't one morning a week. In reality you saw one of the partners in the morning while the other might have been at work, and if they wished to come together you'd have to make an evening appointment. We knew that we'd all have to attend training sessions and case discussions but these were nearly always in the evenings because many of the counsellors were working during the day. So my three hours a morning, one day a week, turned out not to be quite so. But I did enjoy it and I found it most interesting. Many surprises, many daunting and sad situations.

Only one case will I mention which is an example of how, in these situations, part of one's own instinct comes into play. On this particular day the husband of a lady who'd been coming to see me regularly had agreed to come with her. I knew quite a lot about this man and his medical background indicated that he was not a well person and could be violent. I remember saying to the secretary in the office, 'If I ring the bell, would you please come in immediately? Don't think I might want coffee for the clients or tissues or any of the things which we often provide, I might need physical help fast.' In fact, this man did become very angry and aggressive, but as he went to stand up, instead of ringing the bell for help I clapped my hands quickly and loudly towards him. Amazingly he sat down, very slowly, in his chair, looking bemused. I remember thinking, just like a balloon being deflated.

I could only walk now with a zimmer for support. Going to the Marriage Guidance office was quite difficult for me because although I had my Government mini and I could sit in the car, slide across and pull the zimmer into the passenger seat, when I got to the office there were five steps at the front, fairly steep, with a railing on one side. There was no way I could go up them with a zimmer so I had to ask some passer-by to lift it to the top level for me. I would hold onto the rail, sometimes with both hands, and lift my feet, one by one, slowly up the steps. Once on the level then I could manage. I never felt any different from others sitting in a chair of course, since all counsellors mostly sat down when they were with their clients, the only difference in my situation being that I couldn't stand up without my zimmer.

I didn't find that my clients made any comment about the zimmer. I had thought initially, I don't know why, that people might think me not suitable as a counsellor. Which brings me to the point: you do feel so different. First not walking very well, then your balance becoming worse, then walking with a stick, and now being dependent on a zimmer. It was cumbersome, ugly, and I found it made me feel embarrassed. People made light of it, I know, but inside me it was often raining in my heart. I tried not to let that show. I think mostly it didn't.

Talking about the zimmer, on a lighter note: one day I was in the family business, Wilkie's, at Shandwick Place and I'd been trying on different necklaces. You know how you do, you pick one up and put it down, and so it goes on. Finally I thought better of it and went to walk out of the shop. In those days they didn't have the alarm system at the door. I was going along Shandwick Place thinking, what an awful noise. I sometimes thought that the zimmer clanked a bit, but this was worse than usual. As I looked down, there, hanging on one end of my zimmer were six necklaces. It looked as if I'd been shoplifting. I got back into the business as quickly as possible, and explained to the assistant behind the counter what I'd done. Most embarrassing.

At this stage I was learning to become a marriage guidance counsellor when many of my friends were out playing golf and tennis and were involved in different activities which I physically couldn't manage. So when I was invited to be a member of the Scottish Access Committee, and at the same time to be a member of the Access Committee for the City of Edinburgh, I was delighted to have all these new interests which I could manage despite my disability. Before I talk of those different activities, however, I would like to finish about the marriage counselling. Firstly on a lighter note, in that when one evening John was kindly looking after the children I returned home to find him looking so stressed. I mean, he's usually such a very calm person. I said, 'Whatever is the matter?'

'Oh, it's Lisa,' he said.

I said, 'Oh dear, is she sick?'

'No, no,' he said, 'she's not sick. She's been wandering round the house, trailing her toy telephone and begging me to tell her the number of the Marriage Guidance Council, because she wanted to speak to her Mummy.'

Although it was funny in one way, it struck me right through. I thought, Angela, this is not what you wanted. I don't want the girls to be upset and feel I've walked out on them at an important time in their day. I know it has to be so in lots of situations but it didn't have to be for me at that particular time in our lives and I felt selfish that I'd been enjoying it so much, the counselling, and the training. I was doing exactly what I had promised myself I wouldn't – take up some activity which would involve me at a time when it was important to be with the children.

As it happened, my time as a counsellor didn't go on for ever. The training was excellent and I much enjoyed the counselling. I enjoyed the group discussions, and I was much encouraged by the senior counsellors when we had ongoing assessments. I was definitely given to believe that I was doing all right, managing most things in a suitable fashion, and I knew that at the end of two years we would be seen by a psychiatrist whose judgement would be the final sanction on whether we were passing out, you might say, as a marriage counsellor. But it was with some misgivings that I heard that the psychiatrist was to be the same gentleman who saw us at our selection weekend. Stupid, I know, but I was apprehensive.

I arrived at the address given to me and was horrified to find that not only were there steps up to the front door, but also that the room in which I was to see the psychiatrist was up an enormous flight of stairs. There didn't seem to be any way in which it would be possible for me to have the interview on the ground floor. Pretty hard that, I thought, but never mind, get on with it, Angela. Get up that staircase somehow, hang on to the bannister, ask somebody to carry up the zimmer. It took me quite a while and when I got to the top I felt tired before I'd even started the interview. I was shown into a room with very large north facing windows and, there at the end of it, standing with his back to the window, was the psychiatrist. He stepped forward to say hello and invited me to sit in a chair, facing him. He sat down with his back to the window. Immediately I realised that I couldn't see his face properly. It was almost as if he was sitting in the gloaming and I was facing the piercing north light from the window.

The interview started and the psychiatrist didn't seem to be at all interested in my cases. He'd had access to my notes but he didn't ask me any questions at all about those or how I felt, or how I was getting on, or any problems that I had in terms of the counselling. He immediately attacked, yes, I think that's not too strong a word, attacked myself. You may think, whatever do I mean? He repeatedly threw questions at me, about my personal life, our marriage, my emotions, and particularly my disability. He latched on to it, like a clam to a rock. He wouldn't let it go. I tried to answer as calmly as possible but I could feel myself becoming upset inside. Gradually his questions became more serious, to the effect that, didn't I realise that my disability was bound to affect our marriage? that I couldn't possibly expect our marriage could last with such a huge pressure on it. He went on and on, and on a bit more. I could feel myself starting to crack, and as he persisted, I could feel tears pricking the back of my eyes. It wasn't possible to hold on, and yet half of myself was saying, Angela, this is unreasonable, this is not right. But it's extremely difficult when you can't see the face of the person saying these harsh words and you feel as if you're under a microscope.

I came out of there, completely shattered, wrung out, miserable, definitely knowing that he felt I was not, and would never be, suitable as a person to be a marriage guidance counsellor. It was all so contrary to how things were, and to what I had been encouraged to believe by all senior people in the council.

Somehow I got down that large staircase. Going down is more dangerous, of course, extremely so when you're upset and you can't see much when your eyes are blurred with tears. I managed somehow to get into my car and drove back to Craigleith Gardens, thinking, whatever is Judy going to think when I collect the children? I'm such a heap and don't seem to be any use at all. I felt as if I'd been dissected, piece by piece, until there was nothing of me left. I arrived at my brother and Judy's house where Clare and Lisa were being looked after, and somehow, I don't remember going in. I think Judy was kindly watching for me and brought the children out. She must have seen my tears but, wonderfully tactful as she is, she made light of it at the time. Luckily the girls were chattering and didn't notice anything.

CHAPTER EIGHTEEN

So it was that I stepped down from Marriage Guidance Counselling and in a way it was better, although I missed it. At the same time I became involved in access for disabled people as a member of both the Scottish Access Committee and the Access Panel for the City of Edinburgh.

Mr Rogerson, an architect from Glasgow, made a strong chairman of the Scottish Access Committee. You could say he somewhat ruled it. Our remit was not simply to achieve the correct access for those in wheelchairs but also for the deaf, hard of hearing, partially-sighted, blind and those with walking difficulties. I learned quickly that there were several like myself, with a physical disability, on the committee. There was a gentleman in a wheelchair who was a sculptor. There were also two other architects, a lady representing the needs of blind people and at one stage we had a young deaf lady who had her own induction loop system. Usually there were twelve of us; it varied in number, but it always included somebody from the Scottish Office as it was important to have somebody who could represent the decisions of the committee at a higher level. The meetings were often very lively. Mr Rogerson kept us on our toes and alert, as we needed to be.

Mr Rogerson thought it would be a good idea if he went and gave a lecture to some of the architectural students at different universities and he invited me to go along, in a wheelchair, as a practical example. Although I had sat in a wheelchair on only a few occasions my experiences were sharp and fresh in my mind. I went with him to Edinburgh University where we met fifteen students. Mr Rogerson gave them a lecture on the needs of disabled people, whether in homes, hospitals or municipal buildings. They all received what he said extremely well, and then it was my turn to show them the practical problems. For example, how my hands could be caught going through too narrow an entrance, or if the door was so narrow then I couldn't get through at all. Or maybe someone had thought of putting a ramp, but had they thought about the width, the gradient, the need for a handrail and for a non-slippy surface? Then, often bathrooms had been specially adapted, but with rails all round cluttering it up, without thought about who was going to be holding onto them. Were they in the right place and were they strong enough? Things like the height of the toilet. Could the person turn on the taps if they had, for example, rheumatism? Could they reach the light? Was a switch so high up that someone sitting down there couldn't reach? In the lift, what about that? A person might get into the lift, and if they were sitting down, they wouldn't be able to reach numbers for the top floors. They could be completely stuck. We stressed the importance of touch buttons so that a blind person could know which floor they were pressing. Alert buttons in bathrooms were needed, with a pull chord so that someone, if they had a fall, could call for help. Was the mirror in the right place? Was it a good long mirror enabling someone standing up to see in it, but equally a person sitting down to see properly and not just the top of their head? There were many small practical examples which came springing to my mind. I so enjoyed the afternoon. It wasn't hard at all to do what was required of me, because I was living these difficulties.

I had high hopes of those talks to architectural students and I thought that they would never forget the needs of disabled people. That was a very naive thought. I sadly learned that people quickly forget or that, if they remember, then as soon as the plans are into the discussion stage particular needs are the first to go.

I had another practical meeting with the Committee to St Andrews University. We were targeting universities to establish if it was possible for the young disabled person, with whatever difficulty, to be a student. Could they get in? Would they be able to hear? If they were blind, would there be any provision for that? St Andrews, of course, is a famous old town and the buildings are all old buildings and are not in general suitable for disabled people. The day was somewhat of a nightmare for me. Again, I was sitting in the wheelchair. There seemed to be steps everywhere, and even some tall doors were too narrow. You could accept sitting down at the front in the lecture theatre and not being in the tiered positions, but I asked in which residences would someone like myself stay? Well, they were sure they'd thought of that. We were shown round and I do remember that the residences they thought were suitable were quite a way from the centre of the town and it would have been a great problem for a disabled person to get to and fro, or expensive if they had to have transport. I didn't think that was going to be very suitable. No, they now understood why – not! This sort of thing often happened on visits like that.

Another visit was to the Western General Hospital. I thought, this will be fantastic as it is the most modern hospital in the city. I thought, with all the provisions laid down they'll have ramps and special bathrooms and things like that. But again, I was to be disappointed. There was quite a large group of us and we'd been told that the hospital management and medical staff were happy to be meeting with us, that the clerk of works was not pleased about our visit but he had grudgingly agreed to attend. We were shown round the outside of the hospital first and came to the large main entrance of the Oncology department. I was bowling myself along in my wheelchair, with no problem at all. The incline wasn't too steep and I could see ahead where the doors opened and shut automatically. But in front of this door I noticed how the incline had a sudden dip in it. Most people walking along wouldn't be aware of it but I had previously experienced what happens when you're in a wheelchair - you tip backwards.

I held back and said to one of the architects, would he mind waiting for a moment with me?

'Oh,' he said, 'whatever is the matter?'

I said, 'Well, I'll tell you when they've all gone in.'

The other members of our committee and the different representatives from the hospital side, the clerk of works included, all went inside these big electronic doors and, of course, were wondering what on earth this young architect and I were doing outside. I just said to him quietly, 'Will you do something for me? I'm going up this slope, and I want you to have your hands right behind my wheelchair, not touching the handles, but so that the minute I tip backwards, you'll be able to catch me.'

'Oh, good gracious,' he said, 'what are you going to do?'

I said, 'It won't be bad and you'll be there behind me. I won't fall backwards, but I would unless you were there and knew what was going to happen.'

I didn't want to take too long to explain. I didn't want the others inside to guess that I'd planned this. I proceeded forward and up the slope. The automatic doors opened and, as they did so, the little front wheels of my wheelchair met this hollow which had come about through people passing in and out over a number of years. Suddenly, as the little wheels went up from the hollow, I felt my wheelchair tipping back and thinking, wonderful, this young chap's behind me. In front of me were the others standing there, including the clerk of works, their faces aghast. ' Oh my goodness,' they said. All was well, of course. I knew it would be. We went inside and they all stood around. The clerk of works who had been so frosty and difficult stepped right forward.

'I've got it. I apologise, I'm absolutely sorry, I had no idea, but you've shown me in a moment how dangerous that is. I'll have some tarmacing work done tomorrow. I'll make sure that is sorted out.' And he said, 'I'm ashamed to think I was against your visit.'

The word mandatory had become essential over the many years that we'd worked and campaigned. We constantly came up against a brick wall of people who either wouldn't or couldn't provide what was necessary. Finance would usually be at the top of their list. But the fact is that if it's a toilet that's required only one is necessary. Up until then people were providing a male toilet for the disabled and a female one, and the whole thing was ridiculous. Suppose there was someone like myself needing their husband to help them? When people ever challenged me about the idea of a unisex toilet I would always retort, 'Well, we all use the same toilet at home, I can't see the difference.' That always worked. They would say, of course, how silly, I hadn't thought of that. As I've said, people's attitudes can be changed quite easily by keeping explanations simple.

Over the years I didn't find it difficult talking to people about the improvements necessary, but I do admit that along the way I came in contact with several architects, not those from the Committee of course, but others who in my opinion were mostly good-looking, charming and absolutely useless. Rather a strong statement, I know. I don't say all and I don't mean all, but I do mean far too many. It is not enough to pay lip service to access and it's not enough to have the drawings and the measurements correct to get through planning permission. It's the end product that we're looking for and it's no good saying, oh well, the money was cut back a bit, surely a centimetre off the width of the doors won't really make a difference. Of course it makes the difference. It might just be the very difference that will make it impossible for a person to get through that door.

My overall feeling about the work of the City of Edinburgh Access committee would be this. Many people in their own time, voluntarily, worked extremely hard against all the odds to achieve what nowadays people would call human rights or equal opportunities. All these words are bandied about now. It wasn't so then. We didn't mind the hard work at all but there was not a lot of encouragement or support from many people in positions of power who could easily have smoothed the path and improved attitudes, much more quickly and without incurring a lot of funding. I'm talking about attitude. Funding is absolutely no good at all without the right attitude. In my experience it is the most difficult thing to correct. However, I believe strongly that it is up to us who have the difficulties to explain in a pleasant way, not to be confrontational, but to help others understand our various difficult situations.

One day I was phoned up by the local radio station, Radio Forth, and they explained they wanted to do a live programme on the access, or lack of it, in the city. Someone had suggested they could go round with a person in a wheelchair to various locations and see how it worked out. Would I like to be the person in the wheelchair? I thought this might be rather fun. When I asked them where they wanted to go they said, 'Well, we'll go to a cinema, the theatre, try and do a bit of shopping along one of the main streets, and we'll go into a pub.' There were warning bells already sounding in my head, but I was careful to say nothing. I thought it would make a much better programme if they came across each problem in a spontaneous way.

The day dawned and it was pouring with rain; it couldn't have been worse. I knew it was going to be pretty tiring for me, although they would help me of course, getting in and out of the car. The wet always makes these things more difficult.

We started off in one of the big cinemas. I could go and buy a ticket and I could go straight forward to the ground floor cinema, but where was I going to put my wheelchair? There were no spaces for a wheelchair and to place it in the aisle would be a fire hazard, therefore not permitted. If I needed to go to the toilet, where could I go? My chair would not go through the doors of the ladies', and there was nowhere else. Problems one and two.

We then went to a theatre, where there was a totally different attitude. A space had been made for wheelchairs and they had an adapted unisex toilet on the ground floor, and they had a lift, amazing, a lift to go up to the stalls. Yes, extremely forward thinking, the Royal Lyceum Theatre in Edinburgh. A long time ago they had made good provision. There were still many things to be improved, but they had made a start.

I was then driven up to Morningside by these two chaps from Radio Forth with their recording mikes. The rain was still pouring down. They said, 'Well, I think we're going to get a bit wet on this one, Angela, because we want to go along the pavement and we would like to cross at a pedestrian crossing.' I thought, that's going to be dangerous, because my experience of those had not been good. However, I kept these thoughts to myself. They got me out of the car, moving along the pavement, the rain still pouring down, and I was saying how difficult it is to predict how people around you are going to move. You're often insecure in thinking that you might have a collision, and a wheelchair could damage someone's legs and I couldn't bear to think of that.

We arrived at the crossing. They pressed the button and were talking spontaneously on the mike. I was really enjoying it. We went to cross the road. Well, I wasn't going slowly. My arms and hands were strong and I was actively pushing the wheelchair along but we were only in the middle of the road when the light changed to green for the traffic and it started to move. Cars on our right and a bus on our left and these two young men said, 'This is a nightmare, this is positively dangerous.'

I said, 'I'm afraid this is what happens. The timing is quite wrong, it's not

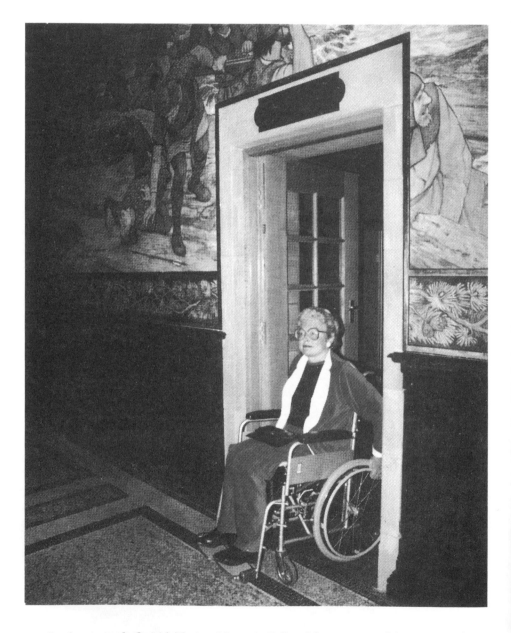

Good access at the Scottish National Portrait Gallery (photo courtesy of Antonia Reeve)

sufficient, and I'm not particularly slow. What about people who are partially sighted or blind, or an elderly person walking with a stick, there's no chance for them to get over in time. And a young mum with a toddler and a baby in a pushchair, she'd be hard pressed to get over in time too.'

We got to the other side of the road, the traffic converging behind us to the extent that we received huge muddy splashes from the bus as it swished angrily past us. We were just on the pavement in time, but not in time to miss the splash. My companions realised then that I was dirty, more so than they were because I was sitting down. They spoke volumes onto the tape. It all came out in a rush, 'This is simply shocking, I don't know how you stand it, how you put up with it. We've got to see things improved and changed. Who understands about these things?'

Finally my two friends said, 'We all need a drink.' Perfect timing for our visit to the pub in the High Street. Wet and muddy as we were, back into the car, but the reward for my morning's effort was not to be. Although we negotiated the steps up into the pub, when asked what I'd like to drink, I paused, wondering, and asking the barmaid, where was the ladies?' 'Oh dear,' she said, 'it's downstairs.' It had been a long morning so sadly my reply to my friend's question was, 'I think I should pass.'

It was an excellent piece of live radio because both their reactions and mine were all fresh and it came to them as a total shock, as indeed it would to people who heard the broadcast. To understand these things people sometimes need a bit of a jolt. Hopefully the listeners received just that.

CHAPTER NINETEEN

That year, 1981, was the International Year of Disabled People. There were two particular incidents that I would like to recount. I was asked to speak at St Andrew's Church in George Street at a Sunday morning service. Daunting. Absolutely. The minister, Andrew Wylie, came to talk to me beforehand, and said he'd leave it up to me to say what I liked. It was a huge challenge and somehow I felt I had to say that I would do it. I was totally unused to speaking in public and I couldn't imagine doing it, but on the other hand I felt he was giving me an opportunity to express what it was really like coping with a disability and thereby giving the congregation a real understanding of the difficulties.

The access to the church was so-so. There was a ramp but getting in to the front of the church where I had to speak from – never mind, we overcame that. I was getting used to overcoming such access problems. It's no good making a fuss all the time: work for the improvements, but don't make a fuss all the time. People become rather fed up with that. I had given considerable thought as to what I might say, but in a strange way what came out at the time was somewhat different. One thing I mentioned was how fortunate we are in this country to have the National Health Service and so much support, and the availability of something like a wheelchair. I put it to them that were I somewhere in the Third World there would be few, if any, wheelchairs. I would be lying in bed twenty-four hours a day, seven days a week, fifty-two weeks a year, shut away from the real world, hidden by whatever family I had, who would be ashamed of my existence. I felt my words sinking in.

In July of that year there was the Royal Garden Party at Holyrood Palace and, because it was the International Year of Disabled People, people like myself who were working to improve things for the disabled were kindly invited to the Garden Party. John and I had this royal invitation. Very exciting. Think of a new outfit. Desperate. A hat – I hate hats. And gloves – oh, even worse. We had a special pass for the parking because of the wheelchair; many things were made easier for us. The weather wasn't desperate, but it wasn't wonderful either. The sky was grey, it threatened rain, and underneath the grass was wet: a bad combination for the wheelchair. I quickly found it extremely difficult to move a wheelchair along wet grass. We could see people congregating in lines and one of the Queen's Archers said, 'This is where the Queen will come and be introduced to people.'

I said, 'Oh, I'd love to see her. To be very close to her would be such a thrill.'

He then kindly said, 'If you follow me, I'll find you a space right at the front.'

It made all the difference. Suddenly there was the Queen, talking to people being introduced to her. Sparkling, vivacious, fun, and full of laughter. We could hear her most clearly. I'll remember that day always.

Then we met people we knew and one of them said, 'What about tea?' That seemed a good idea. The food was delicious. Everything was miniature – the sausage rolls, the sandwiches and the strawberry tarts. But in my situation I found them difficult to handle. The crumbs fell on my dress. I was terrified I would make a mess. When I was trying to handle a strawberry tart, someone insisted that I had a cup of tea at the same time. I couldn't handle the two and didn't know what to do about it. These were all new experiences for me, and not comfortable ones. So the Garden Party, which I'd looked forward to so much, was a mixed experience. The shining light was the Queen. The sadness was recognising in myself my disability.

At this time I was seeing Dr Mawdsley on a regular basis. I could drive myself there and get the zimmer out. It was quite extraordinary how I did that, and I've no idea how I learned to do it, but I would put the zimmer beside the opened door, the passenger's side. I would slide my way slightly to the middle, managing to get my legs over the gear stick, and then I would pull the zimmer into the car and twist it round so that it would sit with the handles over the back of the passenger's seat. Then I could slide myself properly into the driving seat and drive off. On arrival I had to do things in reverse. Reach across, open the passenger door, find a way, which somehow I did, to get the zimmer out and then repeat the return journey across the gear stick, onto the passenger seat and push myself up and out of the car, holding onto the zimmer. Quite a complicated procedure. It was the first of many situations I had to adapt to. But unfortunately my walking, even with a zimmer, was becoming not only more difficult, but definitely tiring. I would arrive for my appointment with Dr Mawdsley and be more than grateful for a seat in his secretary's office before she showed me in.

I enjoyed my visits to him enormously. They were fun, stimulating and interesting, and he always gave me such hope and support. I knew he couldn't wave a magic wand but the fact that he was in charge of me somehow made all the difference. It gave me a confidence to cope with whatever I had to. There were times when he would say, 'I think you need to come into the hospital for a few days and have some physiotherapy and we could run through one or two blood tests. You needn't stay long, because I know it's difficult with the children.'

So there began a time when I had to face that, and John and the girls were wonderful in coping. John and I had this pact that the children wouldn't come much to the hospital unless I could see them in the garden outside the ward. John and I had another pact. As my hospital stays increased we decided it would be much better if John didn't come every night.

Many of our family and friends came to see me. I wasn't without visitors but there was one day when everybody had a visitor in the evening, after supper, and I did not. I wasn't expecting John to come and I was quite happy reading my book until the Staff Nurse came up to me. This shows such lack of tact. You could hardly believe it in a trained person.

'Where's your husband, Mrs Dobbie? Isn't he coming tonight?'

It was obvious that he wasn't since visiting was nearly finished.

'Why not?' she asked, which I thought was most impertinent. She went on questioning me and I said, 'But it's nothing to do with you, and John's been visiting me in hospital for years.' She persisted with several other questions and then swept off. By this time I was upset, not at the fact that I didn't have a visitor, but that she'd spoken to me like that, as if she was implying that there was something wrong with our marriage. When I saw John the next day I told him what the Staff Nurse had said. He was furious, and I'm glad to say he went and spoke to her. I think, to be honest, she just had no idea how insensitive she had been, and hopefully, after John had explained to her, she wouldn't make such a dreadful mistake again.

There were many things in hospital that I had to learn to cope with. The noise at night, the coughing, seeing people much worse than myself, knowing that that might be how I would be. Yes, that was very telling on my mind, on my emotions and was probably one of the most difficult things to cope with. I liked people, being quite a gregarious sort. I found it easy to talk to others but the ward did have many serious neurological cases and it could be very depressing. I would spend as much time as I could in the day room or even outside, if possible. I was fortunate that I could do that. One time, though, I was lying in bed and my legs felt sore and I couldn't move them much. We knew that Dr Mawdsley was coming on his round and there was great activity from the staff to have everybody shipshape and the ward looking neat and tidy, not to mention everybody's bed, made to the nursing specifications and tucked in well and tight, looking pristine on top. I was very uncomfortable as I couldn't move my legs to improve the situation and I thought, I'll have to be stuck like this until the doctors reach me, which could be ages. Two nurses came bustling along the ward and as they passed my bed I took hold of the counterpane and the top sheet and threw both back.

'Whatever are you doing, Mrs Dobbie? We've just got everything ready for Dr Mawdsley coming.'

'Well,' I said, 'it may look all wonderful on top, but I can assure you this is what it's like for me underneath. My legs, they're not positioned properly and they're hurting so much.'

The nurses looked aghast and quickly pulled the curtains round my bed. 'Oh,' they said, 'we're so sorry, we'd no idea.'

I said, 'The most important thing is how the patients are, surely, not how clinically clean and wonderful the beds look.' I said, 'You've got to make sure that for people like myself the bedding is loose and not pressed tightly down either side of my feet and legs. It causes a lot of pain and even though I can move them just a little bit, you had me pinned down like a butterfly.'

'We hadn't thought of it,' they said, 'we'd never thought of it.'

I said, 'Don't worry, I think you'll always remember now.'

'Oh, we will, but definitely we will.'

In no time at all they made me comfortable, replaced the bedding in a nice loose way, but still looking fine, swished the curtains back, and in came Dr Mawdsley.

Sometimes I was put in a single room rather than the ward. It had advantages: at least at night I could have the door shut and the window wide open, whereas in a ward it would be stuffy and hot. I could get more sleep, it's true, but I don't think being in a room on my own was a good idea. There was too much time to think and dwell on the situation and wish you weren't in it, and wonder how John and the littlies were getting on at home. I had a small tape recorder and I remember that I often would play a Ray Conniff tape. It seemed to be a feature of coping with being a patient like that, and I would latch on to a particular piece of music and I would play it over and over again. It somehow soothed and relaxed me and took me out of the world I was in in hospital.

Several times while in hospital I met people similar in age to myself and with similar problems. One friend I made was Sue who was in the other single room and we used to chat together to pass the time. I asked her how she managed at home. Had they made adaptations to their house? Her eyes lit up.

'Oh yes,' she said, 'there's one excellent thing that has just been changed for me. My husband's made a patio outside the lounge doors so that I can go there on my own and sit in the sun.'

I said, 'That must be wonderful for you, have you been enjoying it?'

Her face clouded over. 'Well, no, I haven't yet.'

'Oh,' I said, 'Why ever not?'

'Well, unfortunately there is still a step from the sitting room down onto the patio.'

My heart sank. I thought I must be very careful what I said. Sadly, her husband had made a mistake not making the access level and Sue hadn't liked to make a fuss, but it truly meant she might as well not have had the patio at all. How important it is for those of us who work on the Access Committees to make sure that disabled people and their families are helped to get things right.

It's a very long day in hospital from 5 a.m. until 11 p.m., and then sometimes even longer when you can't get to sleep for the noise. The evening's the worst. It's so very boring having supper between 5 and 5.30 p.m. It seems to make such a long night of it but if you're in a long time you become institutionalised and have to get used to it. Mostly, I was only there for five days at a time. I always had physiotherapy. I felt it was positive to be having that treatment and I enjoyed making the effort myself. Over in the gym they had a long mirror and the physio would make me stand quite a way back from it, hanging on to my zimmer. To my dismay I looked lopsided. I was lopsided. The weakness I had was more to one side than the other and was causing me to stand badly, to be bent over rather than standing upright. She said, 'Now, just take a step forward.' Of course I was holding on to the zimmer. And it's not so much a step at this stage as thinking of bringing one leg forward and placing the foot down, and then the other one. It's not so much like walking as covering a certain distance with difficulty, hanging on to the zimmer, so I was pushing it along rather than lifting it.

When I went home they would continue to give me physiotherapy as an outpatient and I would drive to the hospital, maybe two afternoons or mornings in the week, and that I found extremely tiring, but nevertheless it was an important effort to make. This fact of tiredness was something that was getting the better of me. It was so important to have rests and not to become overtired because the minute I did that, then I felt disabled and not like everybody else. Although I had to use this beastly zimmer to walk with, I was driving my car and doing many normal things: I know, not the golf, nor the tennis, nor the dancing, but in many many situations I felt just the same as everybody else. I always tried my very best to do whatever it was as if I didn't have a disability. Now some may say that's burying your head in the sand and not facing the facts and rather a silly way of carrying on, or being stubborn, or even stupid. I would challenge all of those who think that. For John and me it is our way, it is our way of coping with all that we do have to cope with, to be in the real world as much as possible and in as normal a way as possible.

CHAPTER TWENTY

We missed having a half-term autumn holiday because the girls were having their tonsils out but two weeks later we took them to Crieff Hydro. Unfortunately we found that there were no other families like ourselves. The hotel had been taken over almost completely by a convention for ministers for the Church of Scotland and their wives. Lovely delightful people, but no youngsters for the girls to play with.

However, Crieff Hydro has a lot of facilities. There's a swimming pool, there's the golf course, there's lots of play things for the youngsters and there was something special the girls were dying to do, which was riding. So John made all the arrangements and the following morning we went up to the stables. I was looking forward to seeing the girls up on their ponies and riding off happily. Out came two different-sized ponies for the girls. Very suitable, well-behaved ponies they looked, and then out was brought a horse. I thought, oh well, that's lovely, John's going to have a ride with them. Not at all. John said, 'It's not for me, it's for you. The horse is for you to have a ride with the girls.'

I was horrified but not quite dumbstruck. I said, 'I couldn't, I don't want to, I'm frightened of horses and anyway I'd fall off with my balance not as good as it might be.'

John said, 'I've spoken to the riding instructor and he says he's had many people here who have much more difficulty than you and they've really enjoyed it. He's promised me that he'll go with you on the ride and stay beside you and keep you right on what to do.'

'Oh no,' I said, 'I couldn't.' I was absolutely terrified but at the same time I didn't want to make too much fuss in front of the girls.

John looked at me with one eyebrow raised as much as to say, 'Couldn't you try it?' and I thought, mmm, I suppose, well, I could try it. I couldn't imagine for a start how they'd get me on the horse let alone keep me on it. However, John and the instructor had obviously thought of all this. They picked me up and got me on the horse - no problem. I sat there, highly nervous, trying to keep calm. The instructor was excellent. He said, 'I know you're frightened but

111

just believe in me. I'm right beside you, I'm not going away, and I promise this horse is not going to bolt off.'

My mind jerked back to that terrible time in Australia when the horse I sat on did just that.

'If you could try your hardest to take deep breaths and relax,' he said, 'you may be surprised to find you quite enjoy it.'

I didn't believe him. The girls were happy up on their ponies, and I was miserable up on this horse. But as we went through the woods and he told me exactly what to do, I was amazed to find that I did relax, and I loved it, and I welcomed this wonderful feeling of the circulation in my legs and feet improving with the ride.

When we came back I said to John, 'Well, you sure pushed me into it, but then I would have missed it if you hadn't. I would never in my wildest dreams have thought that I could manage that. Thank you, that was wonderful.'

'Oh, would you like to go tomorrow?' he said.

'Yes,' I said, 'that would be great.'

That was a lesson for me that often we need to be pushed into something that we don't believe we can do. I wouldn't have believed it possible and I would have missed so much happiness. Having enjoyed the ride so much that weekend, I fully intended then that I would take it up when we were back home but somehow I never did and I'm sorry about that. It would have been most beneficial. I could have made the time, but I didn't. It was no one else's fault but my own but I'd like to encourage anyone who has the opportunity, even if they don't fancy it that much, to take it up for all the different reasons which I've just expressed.

Christmas is one of my favourite times of the year and as usual all the extended family met together, a noisy, lively, but happy day, but in January, when everybody was at a slightly lower ebb, I wasn't feeling too marvellous, but managing. My mother had planned a trip to Australia and she was leaving at the end of January for two months. She asked me if I would mind looking after three wonderful azalea plants with, I would say, hundreds of blooms between the three of them. She said they could be in the conservatory. 'If you just water them a little bit, they'll be all right out there.' As you know, I love gardening and it wasn't too difficult for me to get out there so I was happy to look after them, thinking of all the things that she was always doing for me. It was lovely to think that I could actually do something for her.

After she'd left, one night John suggested that I should think about having a few weeks away in the sun myself. I said, 'Well, I couldn't possibly, because you couldn't be expected to manage with the children and everything.'

'Well,' he said, 'we can probably find somebody.' I couldn't imagine who,

Clare and Lisa

but a little bit of me sparkled inside, thinking, wouldn't that be fantastic? Most of me was telling myself, don't become excited, Angela, you can't possibly imagine it happening in terms of cost and all that, and having someone suitable that John and the girls would all like. However, a great friend of ours, Elspeth Cameron, said that she knew of this delightful lady, Betty Vernon, who had helped Elspeth when she and her husband had gone overseas and left the children. Why didn't I ask her? It was all too good to be true when I found out that yes, she was free, and she'd like to come. Absolutely wonderful. So it was arranged that I should fly out to Australia and have about seven weeks away, quite a long time, that, and Betty would stay and look after the children and John.

Plans were made and my flight was booked. Then I got the 'flu a week before, and not only felt awful but was so weak and tired. I was in bed and as far as my doctor was concerned that was where I was to stay. I was due to leave on the night train down to London on the Sunday. On the Thursday I remember thinking, I must get up and try and get some clothes on, even for a short time, because if I don't I'm going to be far too weak by Sunday. I remember with great difficulty getting my clothes on and I was standing in our hall, where we have a long radiator with a ledge over the top. I felt grim so I was holding onto the ledge when Dr Gibbs swept through the front door.

'Well,' she said, 'what do you think you're doing, trying to stand up there, Angela? I told you to stay in bed and I meant it. If you can't do what I say you haven't any hope at all of going to Australia.'

I was so near to tears and tried to explain how I felt I needed to try and stand for a little while to get my clothes on. 'It's far too soon,' she said. 'Back to bed and don't get up properly until I allow it.'

'But,' I said, 'this is Thursday and I'm leaving home on Sunday night to fly out on Monday morning.'

'Well, we'll just have to take one day at a time and hope for the best.'

She was very matter of fact and quite frankly I was far too weak to argue or even be able to continue standing there. I crept back to bed, utterly miserable, definitely feeling I was not going to make this trip. Lying in bed with too much time to think you become drowned from a great wave of miserable emotion washing over you.

I started thinking of stupid little things like, even if I did get to go away, I certainly wouldn't be able to have my hair done, and I'd look a fright, as if that was the most important thing. But I remember ringing my friend Jenny Harrison and saying I was back in bed and so depressed, and when I mentioned about my hair she said, 'Oh, don't worry, I know an excellent person, June, who'll come to your house and do your hair for you and that'll cheer you up.'

Surprisingly, the following day, Friday, I did feel a lot better. Dr Gibbs came in and said, 'Yes, well, I think you should sit out of bed but don't try and do anything. Preserve your energy for what's going to be a wonderful trip but remember you're not going to make it if you disobey me.' It was a bit like being back at school, really, but what a wonderful friend as well as a superb doctor she was. By Saturday I felt stronger and my spirits rose. My hair, I thought, I'll ring that lady, see if she could manage it. She didn't seem to mind a bit. That made a huge difference and by Sunday I was even stronger but with the daunting thought of the long journey that I was going to make on my own. The girls were a bit tearful about me going. John was wonderfully encouraging and Betty Vernon had arrived and was taking over the household. Such a mixture of emotions.

The plan was for me to go on the night sleeper and John's brother Peter would meet me at King's Cross in the morning and take me across to Heathrow where I would fly to Bahrain, Singapore and Sydney. All was going fine. It had been decided that I would take the National Health wheelchair which I had been given to use if I needed it, not that I was using it very often. I was using my zimmer all the time but I did have the wheelchair for any long distance which I felt I might not manage. I'd spoken to my sister Mary in Australia and she said not to worry at all, she would arrange for the hire of a zimmer for me. I was feeling truly excited. We'd booked a sleeping compartment just by the door, making it easy for me to get in. I had the compartment to myself. I had thought about getting undressed and everything but didn't feel that would be a problem, and I had also thought about spending a penny. But I knew there would be a pot under the washhand basin so I intended to use that.

While saying goodbye I felt how marvellous John was to be giving me this opportunity, putting himself last and me first to have all that sunshine ahead of me and hopefully to improve my health.

The train pulled out of Waverley Station on a very dark, cold night. I got undressed quickly and thought, better spend a penny and try and get some sleep. The night conductor on the train had already asked me if I wished tea in the morning and whether I wanted to be woken up at any particular time. I had said, 'Oh yes, please, that would be a help,' and then I would have plenty of time to be dressed ready when Peter met me at the station. Fortunately I'm not a person who locks doors. I'm much criticised about that, but sometimes it's just as well. I got the pot out from under the washhand basin and thought, well that's fine, spend my penny and get into bed. Well, I got stuck. I'd spent my penny but I could not get back into the standing position. I suppose that with all the excitement and it being late at night and not being over the 'flu, I simply didn't have the strength to stand up. So there I was kneeling on the floor, over the pot and I thought, well, I can't possibly spend the night like this. There's only one thing to do, ring the bell. The thought of the male night conductor coming and finding me in such a position was horrific, but I had no choice. I rang the bell and in no time at all came a tap on the door. 'Come in,' I said, in a little voice. 'I'm sorry, I'm so sorry, but I've had the 'flu and I just seem so weak I can't stand up.'

'Now don't you be worrying,' he said, 'don't you worry at all, it happens all the time. I've helped many a person up from such a situation. Don't be shy or embarrassed about it, all part of my job, you know.' He was delightful, so matter of fact, helped me up. It was all over in a moment and he cut out the embarrassment completely.

I didn't sleep much. But in the morning the excitement was absolutely ripping through me to get dressed, to see Peter coming along in that misty-looking early February morning at King's Cross. He took me to the King's Cross Hotel for breakfast, then drove me out to Heathrow airport. There at the Qantas check-in desk, Peter said goodbye. I was lifted into an airport wheelchair, so that my chair would go through with my luggage. It seemed a long wait, sitting in a huge chair which had no hand rims on it. I was therefore stuck in the one place, a weird experience for me. However, I knew that this was a huge adventure and I knew that I would have to experience many different situations because of my weak legs. I felt that whatever I needed to cope with would be worth it to arrive in Sydney. Many people at home, not of course John, never him because he always encouraged me, but quite a number of others had voiced their concern that I wouldn't manage, that it was far too much even to think of going on my own. Luckily for me, probably the way I've been brought up and just the way I am, I didn't see it as a huge problem. I could see that it was a challenge, but that excited me.

One of the hostesses at the airport wheeled me down the long ramp to the door of the aircraft and there I experienced another new situation when they lifted me out of the wheelchair and set me on one of those ghastly narrow seats with straps round my top half and my legs to stop me dropping off so that they could take me along the aisle of the aircraft. I would like to challenge the people who designed them. I know they have to be narrow, that's not the problem, but there's a frightful steel bar which just happens to go right across the base of your spine. I'm quite sure that whoever designed it has never sat on one; they wouldn't stand it for a second. I was fortunate that they'd given me a seat right at the bulkhead so I would have good leg room. That's not allowed nowadays. They feel that, understandably, someone like myself might be a hazard if they want to use the exit in an emergency and they make people sit one row back. Later on I was able to have my feet up on some luggage and that made all the difference. I was beginning to get tired but looking forward to dinner. Yes, the thought of a drink and some dinner was wonderful. That's always excited me, eating when I'm travelling. Most people say it's boring and they don't like it, but I usually enjoy it and I did indeed. Fortunately I was able to get up and, by holding on, just make the few yards that it was to the toilet. That was one of the main reasons they'd given me that seat so it wasn't a problem on that journey.

I enjoyed my dinner and thought I'd listen to some music until we got to Bahrain, which was going to be in the early hours of the morning. I'd decided that it wasn't fair to ask people to lift me out of my seat and onto the carrier seat, down the steps and into a wheelchair to go into the concourse at the airport, but that was an unwise decision; it's always better to get off. So I stayed on the aircraft while it was being cleaned, a bad decision that. But I was learning, had everything to learn about travelling with a disability. However, the stewardess was very kind when the new crew came on, and when everyone was on board they allowed me to have my feet up and I did get some sleep on the next stretch to Singapore. At Singapore I stayed on the aircraft again and knew I'd only got another seven or so hours to go and we'd be flying into Sydney. Sydney looked dark, but the sky behind was becoming lighter and lighter, and suddenly I saw the lights and then Sydney Harbour Bridge. I felt such an emotion, I could feel my eyes filling with tears. I was so happy I could hardly handle the happiness of flying into Australia, to have the chance to be there again after all those years, and to see everyone who was so special to me.

We landed fine and then, of course, there's always such a wait. If you need a wheelchair, Patience with a capital P. You have to be last off. They lifted me out carefully and then there was the excitement of meeting Mary and Michael, her husband, who had come to the airport for me. They took me off in my wheelchair with the luggage and packed me into the car. By this time the sun was up and it was a beautiful day. I'd been transported from a dark misty and very cold place to a light hot sunshine world. One of the first things that struck me through my excitement was the colour of the dirt, the soil. It looks red somehow, and there are all those wonderful different trees which I've spoken of before, the gum trees and all the fabulous flowers. I felt like a little child with such excitement and not knowing which to enjoy most, first. And I had everything to share with Mary and Michael and was looking forward to seeing my mother again as well. Their little boy, Duncan, I hadn't met either. I quickly realised that the clothes I'd travelled in would end up probably in the suitcase and not come out again. Suddenly I saw everything with a different eye. Clothes that seemed quite lightweight in Scotland were just not on in Australia. Dive for a sundress, get that on, much more the thing. Wear the minimum and be comfortable. We're always rushing to be in the sun if it's out at home. We hate to think we might miss it. But there in Sydney, in the middle of their scorching summer, you are better to keep in the shade as much as possible. I found that quite difficult to begin with, it seemed such a waste of sunshine.

I was keen to try out the zimmer Mary had hired for me. I took one look at it and realised that it wasn't at all like the one I had at home. That didn't matter. They put it in front of me as I sat in the wheelchair, and I stood up holding onto it. That was fine, the height of it was fine. Oh good, I thought, this will be perfectly all right. I went to walk forward. Now, I know I was tired and I'd had the 'flu, and it was slightly different, but to my horror this particular kind of zimmer had shepherds' casters on the front, rather like those wheels on a supermarket trolley, and when I tried to go forward the wheels would go to the right or to the left. To begin with, I thought, Angela, it's just because you're tired and you've had a long journey, and all this excitement. I said, 'I think I'll leave it for now and try again in the morning.' I was so tired, but I didn't sleep much. Jet lag, it does take days sometimes.

However, the next day I was determined that I'd manage with the zimmer and I was sure it would be all right. I had another go, seriously I tried it. I tried it on my own so I wasn't shy or thinking people were watching me. It just would not go where I wanted it to, which made the whole situation extremely hazardous. I asked Mary, 'Do you think there'd be any other kind that I could try?'

She said, 'I'm sorry, no, Angela, this is the only kind they have here but I'll check with the physiotherapist.'

I thought, right, that's it. I sat back in the wheelchair and I thought, okay, I'll have to use the wheelchair for the entire time I'm here.

I didn't, in fact, have a lot of time to think about that. To be truthful, because I'd had the 'flu, I was still suffering from jet lag and I was still tired, my legs seemed awfully wobbly, and I was happier sitting down in the wheelchair. And as the first few days passed by, I learned, to my surprise, I could do more sitting in the wheelchair and bowling myself along than I could with the zimmer. I was able to stand up, to get in and out of bed, to use the bathroom, to get in and out of a car. The wheelchair folded up neatly and went into the boot. We went out one day on a shopping spree to Sydney. Aunty Jean took us and she was appalled that the city didn't have better access for the wheelchair. When we drew up at the kerb outside David Jones', there was this huge, huge step up onto the pavement. They have to keep very deep gutters in Australia to cope with the storm water they often have, something I'd never thought of.

Aunty Jean felt cross that the Sydney authorities hadn't thought of it and she said, 'Well, however do people manage?'

I said, 'Don't worry, Aunty Jean, we'll manage somehow.'

Somebody helped get my wheelchair up on the pavement from the road. Lots to learn about all of that. But we had a whole day in Sydney, in different stores. We had lunch out, I had a wonderful time and I wasn't tired, despite the fact that I had been feeling tired up until that day. I couldn't remember the last time I'd been out shopping for a whole day at home. The fact was that with the zimmer I'd been struggling and was truly too tired to cope with more than a short time and would then have to go home. So there I was now, using the wheelchair all the time but instead of my world closing down, it opened up. I could enjoy all sorts of things and not be tired. The fact that the zimmer wasn't right for me was one of the best things that ever happened. A very strange statement, you might say, but it forced me to accept the wheelchair and in doing that it enabled me to leap a huge emotional barrier which might have taken me several years to cross.

Mary and Michael were very preoccupied with their Amway business which they ran from home. Mother and I were most fortunate to enjoy a week at Aunty Jean's fabulous home at Clareville where we lazed on the beach. I spent hours in the water and then we played bridge at night.

After a short spell back with Mary and Michael, Mum and I went to Aunty Helen and Uncle Peter Fitzsimons, to their lovely rambling house, Windhill, surrounded by their orchards of oranges, lemons and grapefruit trees, with tomatoes growing in between. As always, it was a delight for me to be with this lovely family. However, at the same time, there were many fearful memories which came rushing back to me. The day of the fire, and the dreadful way in which Aunty Helen was burnt, the nightmare of it all, and I couldn't help my eyes going up towards her neck and her ear and the side of her head where she'd had to have many skin grafts after that terrible event. I think it's true to say that something dreadful often brings people closer. It isn't by any means the only reason that Aunty Helen and Uncle Peter and their family have always been special to me, but to this day I often think of what Aunty Helen would have said or done and try to act accordingly.

So there I was back at Windhill. It was hot. But down at the dam where I could have had a swim was not a very easy place for me to have access to, and certainly not from a wheelchair. In the country I suddenly felt more conscious of being in a wheelchair. The tracks are rough and getting around the fruit farm was not exactly like pushing myself along a made-up pavement or a road. I was lucky that my arms and shoulders were strong. I found that the driveway through their garden to different parts of the property was fairly hard and baked by the sun. They hadn't had rain for quite a while, so that was a definite help to me, and I realised it was going to make a huge difference to getting around. Suddenly there were all these things to learn about being in a wheelchair. It was another house to learn how to get in and out of; the bathroom was not quite so easy there, but I just managed to get through the door. I thought, wouldn't it be wonderful to sleep out one night on the verandah and I asked Aunty Helen if I might do that. 'Well, absolutely no problem at all, as long as you don't mind the mossies. We have got a mosquito net but you're going to need that anyway whether you're in or out.' Memories returned of when we were kids down at Newport a long time ago. With my passion for the outdoors and the fresh air, to be on the verandah would almost be like sleeping under the trees because the lovely gum trees come right up to the house. Whenever I am at Windhill, I always feel I could be there forever and be totally happy.

I wanted to learn more about Australian wild flowers. Windhill was exactly the right place to do that. Aunty Helen suggested that we go down the back, through the bush, towards the dam. I was sitting in my wheelchair and she was having to push me along because the track was very narrow and bumpy.

'Let's stop here,' said Aunty Helen, 'and we'll just look at a small area of the

With Auntie Helen FitzSimons on the verandah at Windhill

bush around your chair.' She said, 'I wonder if you can guess how many wild flowers I can point out to you in such a small space.'

I had no idea, I guessed maybe three. Not at all – more like a dozen. She would pick me a small piece and give me the name of each one, mountain bush berries, Star of Bethlehem, flannel flower, Sturt's desert pea, kangaroo paw, mountain devil, hovea and Australian bluebells, to name but a few.

'Would you like me to press them in a book for you with their names and you could take them back to Scotland?'

I felt as if we were in a special world all on our own surrounded by gum trees with their different colours of bark and variety of grey-green foliage. The joy to crush the leaves in my hands and smell the eucalyptus. And then suddenly I thought, gracious, every time people go through the bush they're trampling down these beautiful flowers. We've no idea what we're squashing with our feet or even worse, the wheels of my chair. That moment my chair seemed bulky and even worse than people's feet. We went further on down and came in sight of the dam. It looked so inviting. I would have given anything to go in the water. But the sides of the dam were quite steep and I couldn't see how my wobbly legs would cope with that. I thought, even if I got in slithering down on my backside, it would be somewhat muddy and getting out would be quite impossible.

At that moment Aunty Helen said, 'I've thought of something, Angela. I realise how much the water could help you. A friend of mine lives not far away, Tressa Kemp. She has a beautiful pool and I'm sure we could go and swim there. We'll phone her tonight and ask her.'

The following day we went to Tressa's house. It was even hotter than the day before. I had my costume on and lots of sun cream. I thought, this will be heaven. I'll have a long hot bake beside the pool, which looks most inviting. It was an attractive bungalow, but there was no shade, which surprised me. Foolishly, I sat in my wheelchair in the full baking sun and got hotter and hotter, and then I thought, I'll have that delicious swim. I was able to lower myself out of the wheelchair and sit on the edge of the pool and get in quite easily. There were shallow steps, so getting out was not going to be a problem. Well, of course, I was so cooked, the water felt freezing but I stayed in the water for ages. I did not want to come out. The freedom of it, gliding smoothly through the water after all that bumping around on rough tracks on the fruit farm! What a thrill to be able to swim strongly despite the stupid legs. I think Aunty Helen and Tressa were quite surprised at how much I could swim. Unfortunately the water was highly chlorinated and when I eventually came out I realised that I needed a shower.

Tressa said, 'I'm a little worried about my shower, Angela, there's nothing for you to hold on to and I wouldn't like you to slip and fall.'

I thought, well, I'll have to think about that. Suddenly I thought, we'll take the cushion off my wheelchair and I'll sit in it. 'And then what?' said Aunty Helen.

'Well then, if it's all right with Tressa,' I said, 'I'll just go right into the shower.'

'Oh, it's on the level,' she said, 'it's more than possible, but what about the wheelchair?'

Oh well, it will just have to thole it, I thought. Good Scots word that. They were quite amazed, both of them. So I sat in my wheelchair and had an excellent shower. My wheelchair was totally soaked and I thought, oh well, rust coming up any minute. Not exactly good news for the chair but maybe Uncle Peter will grease it up.

As I've said, the wheelchair was not spoiling my holiday at all. It's true I would have preferred to be walking but it was wonderful to be free of that clanking noise of the zimmer.

One morning in the kitchen Aunty Helen and I had been baking. It was amazing what I could do sitting down. It's true I had to be side on to things quite often but it didn't seem to be too much of a problem. Well, when I had finished helping her with the baking, Aunty Helen was doing some ironing, then went to answer the phone. The place was in comfortable chaos. I thought, I'll just go over to the other side of the breakfast room and have a look at the newspaper. It's fun to catch up on the local news and feel part of the country. I wheeled myself across the room, not noticing the cable for the iron was lying on the floor and not knowing, of course, that it was still switched on. As my wheels reached the cord for the iron a fire broke out underneath my wheelchair. I didn't know whether to go forwards or backwards. I was absolutely terrified. Immediately Aunty Helen came and switched the iron off. That moment I thought, oh no, not more fire, not here, I couldn't handle it. I felt quite unable to cope with it, thinking I was stuck in the wheelchair, unable to jump out of it or run away; I felt trapped. It made me face the fact that sitting in a wheelchair I couldn't move quickly like other people, something which I hadn't thought of until that very moment.

After Sydney I went to stay with my cousin Helen, her husband John Sides and their children on their sheep station in southern New South Wales. One of my greatest delights was to go out when they were rounding up the sheep and I enjoyed seeing kangaroos. Now this is difficult because up there the kangaroos are so destructive. They trample down the fences which causes a big problem to the graziers and they invade people's property, particularly anything like a vegetable or flower garden. They are powerfully strong and the country people go out on raids to shoot them. One evening I went with John while he inspected some fencing. The sun was setting and as it sank right down beyond the flat horizon we could see a herd of kangaroos silhouetted against the vast quickly-colouring sky. At that moment I wished I was able to paint but the memory will stay with me always.

Helen and John had a huge swimming pool and, after a timid start doing only widths, I was doing lengths and managing just fine. It was excellent exercise for me and one Saturday I said to the boys, 'Well, how about a race?'

'A race?' they said, looking slightly embarrassed.

I said it would have to be a race with certain conditions. 'Since I can't use my legs, you'd have to promise not to use yours and agree on the stroke.'

'Oh well,' they said, 'that's not a problem, that's fine.'

Helen was delighted to be the starter and the boys were thrilled and sure they were going to win. I thought they would probably win too but they found their speed in the water greatly reduced by the fact that they were not allowed to use their legs. To my enormous delight I managed to beat them in some of the races, not always of course, because they quickly got the hang of it and they probably had more powerful shoulders than myself, but it was wonderful for my morale to be swimming those lengths up and down and to have the challenge of these young fit people actually racing me in the pool, and to be swimming daily.

Those were happy days and the kids' excitement at what I could achieve matched my own. I felt so much the same as everybody else. Indeed, all that I was doing on this holiday was helping me to be in what I call the real world and to forget that I had ongoing problems. My legs were getting weaker, but the sun was doing me such a lot of good. Looking back to when I left Edinburgh with the 'flu, my general health had improved and the swimming strengthened the muscle power that I still had.

I missed John and the girls and was eager to receive letters but John was not a great correspondent. I phoned up sometimes and was happy to learn that all was going well and that Betty Vernon was, in fact, fabulous and John was enjoying her company because she's got such a good sense of humour, and the girls adored her. So I had no worries, which made a special difference to me, but I still felt guilty about being away.

Back to Sydney, saying all my goodbyes, and the homeward journey with my mother, with a stop-off in Hong Kong on the way. We were to arrive home on Clare's sixth birthday and I promised her that I would be home on the day. We'd worked it out with the flights that, yes, all being well, we'd make it.

We were staying at the Sheraton Hotel in Hong Kong. My eyes were out on stalks at all the sights I had seen in books or on postcards that were suddenly there before our eyes. It is a city teeming with people, full of colour and movement and everything so different. We have a great friend, Peter Stevenson, who lives in Hong Kong. There was a wonderful arrangement in our hotel room of long-stemmed red roses with a beautiful card from Peter and his wife Nobuku welcoming us to Hong Kong, wishing us a very happy time there, and saying that he would be happy to meet with us and give us any help that he could.

We rang Peter and he said, 'I'll come over in the morning after breakfast and I can put you right on where to shop, where to go and definitely where not to go.' He also gave us an excellent rundown on how to bargain in the shops. 'You'll hear a lot of sales talk,' he said, 'but just quarter the price and offer them that.' We thought, this is amazing. Would that really be accepted? But he was insistent that we did this and so we set off that first morning in Hong Kong, me pushing myself along in the wheelchair and my mother with me. We had to remember that she was not used to me being in the wheelchair all the time as I'd been only using the zimmer back in Edinburgh, so it was a new experience for her also. The shopping was fabulous.

I bought some lovely clothes for myself but I particularly wanted to get a birthday present for Clare. I know she was only going to be six but she'd said, could she have a watch? Well, they seemed to be so cheap in Hong Kong. I chose one with great pleasure to take home for her birthday. Everything seemed so reasonable. I went quite mad. I also bought an emerald bracelet and earrings to match. I spent a lot of money, which is not something I had ever done before, but it seemed such an opportunity in Hong Kong. In fact, I became rather carried away. I wasn't thinking about how much you were allowed to take back into the UK, that didn't come into my thinking. We much enjoyed a visit to Peter and meeting his delightful Japanese wife Nobuku. Scotland, and even Australia, seemed a very long way away.

On the evening we left my excitement was mounting about seeing John and the girls. The flights, thank goodness, were good. The only trouble was that we arrived in London just a little bit late and I knew that we were pushed for time to catch the shuttle up to Edinburgh. We identified our luggage. Thank goodness the wheelchair was there. I sat in it and a porter pushed me. He said, 'You're going to be very tight for time to catch this shuttle to Edinburgh.' Suddenly he said, 'Now which light do you want to go through, the red or the green? The red or the green? Hurry up and make up your mind,' he said, the red being to declare, and the green for nothing to declare. My panic was instant, knowing how many things I had in my suitcases. I was not even able to think of adding up the cost and when I read the notice which said how little you were allowed to bring in, I thought I should definitely be going through the red channel. 'Hurry up, hurry up,' he said, 'we must get you on to the shuttle, you're never going to make it. Which light do you want?'

'The green,' I said, 'the green.' My head told me, Angela, this is a nightmare, you're not a dishonest person but you are sure being one right now. We were now almost going at a running pace, my mother keeping up well with this porter and another porter who was pushing the luggage trolley. Along on our left-hand side there seemed to be an endless row of tables with customs officers standing behind them. I thought, I'm never going to get through this. The porter was wonderful. 'We're heading for the Edinburgh shuttle, we need our time,' he said. I must have looked guilty, I surely felt it. Nobody challenged us. We made it to the shuttle. But I will never again come through the customs on the wrong light. It was just too nerve-racking.

We landed safely in Edinburgh and had a wonderful reunion with John, Clare and Lisa. They couldn't believe how brown I was and teased me that I spoke with a slight Australian accent. There was so much to share, especially with it being Clare's birthday. She wondered, had I brought a present? I was glad I'd brought that watch, it meant a lot to her. I explained to them later how we nearly didn't manage to get back in time for the birthday.

CHAPTER TWENTY-ONE

Seeing me sitting in my wheelchair for everything was a shock to John and the girls, our family and friends. I could now stand only briefly providing there was something to hold on to. I had gone away walking about, although with much difficulty, but I was nevertheless at the same height as everyone else. Suddenly my perspective of people, of objects around me and of the world we live in, was totally changed. Being on holiday had smoothed the way for the learning situation which I found myself in with the wheelchair.

Now at home I noticed for a start the step at our front door and with even more unhappiness, the fact that our lovely terrace at the back where we get so much sunshine, also had one step down. It was no problem with a zimmer but hopeless in a wheelchair on my own. These situations became a priority to sort out if I was to have independence at all in going freely in and out of our own home and enjoying the garden. We found that we could have a wooden ramp made for the terrace. We found also that we could have money from the council towards a ramp at our side door, which brings us straight into the kitchen. The worktops in the kitchen were now too high. I couldn't sit at the sink straight on; I couldn't reach the cupboards, particularly the high ones, any more. The oven was hopeless; it was too low. I could reach the fridge, some of it but not all. The freezer likewise. Suddenly doors opened onto me and I wished that they'd all been sliding ones. Things that had never mattered before were simply ghastly now. Quickly we realised that the best thing to do, if possible, would be to change the kitchen for my needs to allow me to be in control and able to cook and carry on as usual. My hands were fine, it was just that I had to sit down now to do everything.

We decided to do the kitchen, a major issue for any family. A very kind neighbour, Sylvia Butters, said she would lend us her caravan and I could have it parked at our front door where we had plenty of driveway and I could cook in that. It had two steps but I still had the power to pull myself up and because the caravan was so small there was always something to hold onto inside. Cooking in a caravan, with a disability and no water, even though I was outside my own house, was fraught, but I managed. One evening I went round in my

126

wheelchair to peer into the kitchen. The builders had all the drains up and were re-laying pipes. They'd left the kitchen door open so that the bricks they'd been setting for the big picture window could dry out. A major feature of this new kitchen was not only to have everything at the right height but also for me to be able to see our beautiful garden from the sitting down position. This had been one of the main priorities in discussing design with the architect and the builders. Earlier that day I had been a bit anxious when watching the builder lay the bricks for the window. I couldn't go in but the base for the window looked awfully high to me, so when they'd gone and before John returned home, I went round the side and peered in again. My heart sank. I felt sure I was not going to be able to see out, unless I craned my neck. When John came home I could hardly wait to ask him to come and have a look. The builders had left two planks and John carefully pushed my wheelchair up the planks to get me into the kitchen so I could gauge properly if I could or could not see out. It was instantly obvious to both of us that the answer was, no. I felt so disappointed and upset. John felt furious and was angry. He went to the telephone, he rang the architect, he rang the builder.

He said, 'We're spending all this money to get this particular thing right and it's not right. We know the kitchen's not finished but we can see at this stage that the window is not going to be low enough.'

I think John paid the architect's fee and said we would no longer need his services, he was so angry. The next morning the builder returned and we showed him, with me sitting in my wheelchair, that they must have got their measurements wrong. 'Yes,' he said, 'we have, for some reason. It was all done carefully but you're right, we'll have to take out those bricks and reset them so that the whole window will be lower.'

That was one of my first experiences of things going wrong when trying to achieve the right facilities for my needs. It gives such a mixture of emotions because as the person who has this disability, you feel bad in the first place for creating the need for change, not to mention the cost. You feel you're putting everybody involved to a lot of bother, even though they go to great lengths to tell you that you're not. Inside yourself, I must tell you, you feel bad about it. And in a curious awful way of mixed emotions, half of you wants to say, 'Oh well, don't worry, anyway, it'll be all right,' or 'It doesn't matter,' and the other half is screaming, 'Don't say that, Angela, it does matter and it won't be all right and unless you speak up politely but clearly, it will never be right.' It's tiring, those emotions, stressful, and disappointing when you've placed your confidence in people who are going to make your life easier. I was certainly learning the gut feelings fast.

The good news was that we did create an attractive and practical kitchen, with the double-glazed picture window onto our garden, the split-level oven, the lower sink, and the other facilities which I needed. There was a round kitchen table in the middle where I could sit with the family and friends and feel the same as everyone else. I know I keep saying that, but my goodness, it is important, it means such a lot to feel the same as everybody else.

One day, to my great surprise, somebody said to me, when I had confessed quietly how in a wheelchair you can feel in the way and clumsy, 'Oh, but I don't think of you in a wheelchair, Angela; I don't think of you in a wheelchair at all.'

I was truly amazed at that. At first I couldn't believe it, but then I realised she was sincere. However, that was not the case for me, seeing myself in a mirror sitting in the wheelchair was something I had a long way to go in handling. That took me years and even now I have my moments.

Before I leave the kitchen and our changing it, I'll mention the ramp. The builder had had an excellent idea that we'd make it a concrete ramp with sloping sides, moulded in a way that would not trip people up. I was anxious that adaptations necessary for me were not going to make our home ugly, or awkward for others. He made this excellent concrete ramp and I have it to this day: the correct gradient – 1 in 12 – ridged so as not to be slippery, but still we made a huge mistake. It wasn't until the job had been finished completely that we signed the form and applied for the funding which we understood we would receive to pay for this ramp. 'Oh, I'm very sorry, we can't give you any money,' the council said. 'You should have sent us two builders' quotes and given us the chance to choose, and then we might have funded this adaptation for you.'

And then, of course, the bathroom. We had to do something about that, which led us rather to think of extending our bedroom and having a bathroom en-suite. That took a lot of money and a lot of patience. It gave us much stress, including a lake behind our house where there had been a driveway before. There was water under the house, but the insurance company was wonderful and paid for that. We needed new joists and flooring for the eastern end of the house. But in the end we created a wonderful large bedroom with French doors facing south to the garden, a large window facing east and another one facing north and a bathroom en-suite. It created space, which is a happiness if it's possible to have it. Without it you definitely feel in the way in a wheelchair; you knock into things, damage things, and upset people although they try not to show it. We now had a spacious bedroom with a beautiful outlook and our own bathroom in which we'd taken care to make the vanity unit all accessible for me and space beside the loo so that I could easily have my wheelchair in there and use the facilities.

Another problem that I had to resolve was how to get around our home to do some dusting and clearing up, even though I did have help three mornings a week. I liked doing it and I wanted to. The clearing up after a family in the morning once they've swept out to work and school: we all know what that is like. Glasses, mugs, papers, all sorts of things dropped on the floor and left lying about. Clothes need collecting up and putting in the machine. One day I latched onto the idea that I could push the trolley along in front of me using the footplates of the wheelchair and load things up upon it. It had two levels which gave me increased space. This was absolutely marvellous. I would go round the house with this trolley, taking care not to knock the paintwork, and collect all sorts of things. Anything breakable I would put on the top and things like washing I would put on the bottom shelf.

One particular morning I wasn't too careful about where I put anything; I suppose I was in a rush. In those days we had a Goblin Teasmade. We enjoyed morning tea in those precious moments when you wake up and still have time to lie there without getting out of bed immediately. I took the teapot from its machine and put it on the top of the trolley together with our mugs and other bits and pieces that were lying beside our bed. I then collected up some clothes and didn't notice very carefully where I put them on the trolley. I went through into the sitting room, collected newspapers and more general pieces of rubbish, and eventually arrived back in the kitchen. I picked up the washing with both hands and threw it on the floor. There was a terrible crash, not to mention a brown liquid coming out from under the clothes across the kitchen floor. I realised instantly that I had picked up the teapot, full of tea leaves. What a mess. Tea leaves stick to everything and the tea was staining our clothes. I never made that mistake again. It seemed funny at the time, although there was no one to laugh with since I was on my own.

I didn't mind being on my own. We were all brought up as very independent people and I needed my independence; I didn't want to lose that. I was trying in every way to keep it. This brings me to my Mini car. I managed getting in and out of it with a zimmer, but a wheelchair is another matter. I didn't think at first that I'd ever get the wheelchair into the Mini, the boot is so hopelessly small. But if the front passenger seat was tipped forward it was possible to fit this neat wheelchair which I had in behind the passenger seat but, of course, I needed somebody to do that for me. Well, I thought, maybe I could keep one in the car and get out of the driver's side into the second wheelchair which I used at home. The vehicle centre were wonderful about allowing me to have two. It's true that when I arrived wherever I was going it did require me to ask someone to help lift out the wheelchair, but people are excellent and I always made sure to ask first if they had any back problems, in which case I would ask someone else.

It wasn't only the independence which driving continued to give me, it was this tremendous thrill of being behind the wheel and being able to move at speed. When you're sitting down for everything, the speed of your life physically is reduced to such a little. I missed it, I missed the feeling of the wind in my face that you get when you run forward. I craved that feeling of air rushing past. In the car I mostly felt the same as everyone else and felt that other people wouldn't know that I had to sit in a wheelchair. It sounds so vain, all of this, but these were the emotions that I felt at the time. As the disability increases you have to learn patience. I never had been very patient. I think it's true to say that few of my family are patient people but after many years I have had to learn patience and to remain inwardly calm when all things around me would make me feel not only impatient but upset and angry. You can't afford these emotions because they're too tiring. It doesn't get you anywhere, it doesn't help people around you. It only makes you more of a burden to them, or so I've always thought. Before I leave this word patience I'd like to put in this: that of everybody I know, John is the person with the most patience and understanding and self-control, and I thank him from the bottom of my heart.

CHAPTER TWENTY-TWO

Another year was going by; the girls were happy at nursery and primary school; we had all our social activities and our family outings. I wasn't feeling all that wonderful and weight-bearing on my legs had become very difficult. Dr Mawdsley thought that he would try me on another course of dexamethasone which had helped me before. He arranged for me to go into hospital.

As far as I understood it I was just going into the Northern General Hospital for a week's physio, the steroids, and some rest. I was finding the customary chest x-ray on admission an irritation in that I felt it was an unnecessary exposure to radiation. I was there for treatment of my legs and nothing to do with my chest. However, you do as you're told. After the chest x-ray I was taken back to my room just off the ward, but before long the porter came back with his large chair and said, 'I'm sorry, Mrs Dobbie, but you'll have to come back to x-ray.' I thought, oh dear, I must have moved or they've made a mess of it.

So here we were again, more exposure to x-rays and I thought the whole thing was completely unnecessary. However, this time it was the senior radiographer who came into the room and she said, 'Now, Mrs Dobbie, I'd like you to be up on the big flat table please.'

Immediately I said, 'Oh, is there not some mistake? I've just come for a mini chest x-ray on admission.'

'Now, Mrs Dobbie, I don't want to discuss it. The doctors want to have a different type of x-ray and I'd like you to co-operate please.'

They helped me to get up on the hard table, which I found quite painful, and inside myself I was boiling. I thought, this is ridiculous, I'm sure they've got me mixed up with somebody else. I started to argue again with the radiographer who became extremely cross.

'I have got better things to do than argue with you, Mrs Dobbie. These x-rays have been ordered by Dr Mawdsley.'

That shut me up. I lay there and they took a number of x-rays, quite different from mini chest x-rays. Having had nurse's training I knew a little of what they were doing. They were taking tomograms, that is, pictures of my chest in layers. I couldn't understand it but I kept silent. I was there for about forty minutes and then I went dutifully back to my room where I sat feeling totally confused.

After quite a while the door opened and in walked Dr Mawdsley. He shut the door behind him. He had the large brown envelope of the x-rays under his arm. He pulled up a chair and sat down. I thought, this looks serious.

'Well,' he said, 'Angela, you're not going to believe this.'

To which I replied, 'I think I'd believe anything, Dr Mawdsley.'

'No, I understand, I knew you were going to feel like that, that's why I brought the x-rays and I'm going to put them up on the plates there and put the light on and I'll be able to show you what I'm talking about.'

'But what is that?' I said.

'Just a moment,' he said, as he clipped the x-rays up to light them. 'Now, look at this. These are your lungs on these two x-rays.'

I couldn't believe it. They both appeared to be full up with what looked like cotton wool. I said, 'But what is the matter with me?' I said, 'I haven't got a cough, I don't feel poorly except I have felt tired, but that's not unusual.'

'Now, if you look a little closer,' he said, pointing to the x-rays, 'you'll see the gland in the middle, the mediastinal gland is enlarged.'

'Oh yes,' I said, when he pointed it out.

'I think this is the answer,' he said.

'The answer to what?' I asked.

'Well, I think you've got sarcoidosis.'

'And whatever is that?' I said.

'Well . . .' and immediately I interrupted, 'Surely what I've got already is enough without this too?

'Oh no,' he said, 'it isn't this as well, this is it.' He said, 'This, I believe, is what you've had all along and we've not understood it, but now we've got the proof seeing your x-rays, and this gland enlarged, and it fits in with the way you've responded all these years to steroid treatment and to the tests I've given you at different visits. You've always seemed to be flaccid instead of spastic and your various reflexes on testing were different to what I was expecting. It all fits in, now, the puzzle fits in.'

I felt very quiet. All these years I had been diagnosed with multiple sclerosis and now this excellent neurologist, whom I trusted absolutely, was telling me that I had something else with a very unpronounceable name, which I had never heard of despite my nursing training. I said, 'But what will it mean?'

'Well,' he said, 'we'll soon clear up your chest and now we know why you've been responding neurologically to the steroids so spectacularly.' He continued, 'I'm going to have a word first of all though with the chest specialist because I have to tell you that at this moment, Angela, they think you've got TB. Sarcoidosis looks exactly like TB on an x-ray.'

'Ah, yes,' I said, remembering vaguely what TB looked like on an x-ray. All this fuzzy cotton wool stuff in people's lungs. It's very different when it's your own lungs that are up there on the picture.

He left the room and I sat there totally stunned. I didn't know what to make of it at all. Various nurses came in and out and I was shocked, I suppose, numbed, and I didn't in fact feel anything. I didn't know whether to be pleased or sad; I didn't know what it would mean. I didn't know if it was a better thing to have than what I'd been told all those years ago, or worse. But what came next was another surprise. Dr Mawdsley returned with the chest specialists and they all spoke about me and to me, and withdrew again, and then Dr Mawdsley came back and said,

'Angela, the chest specialists are determined that this is TB and we're going to do one or two tests to see if we can find out if you have tuberculosis.'

And immediately I said, 'Well, I don't feel as if I've got TB. I nursed some very serious TB cases years ago and I had the proper inoculations. In fact, I don't feel as if there's anything the matter with my chest, quite honestly.'

'I know,' he said, 'I know it's extremely difficult, but if you can be patient and trust me,' which of course I did absolutely. But what came next confused me badly.

A couple of days later he said, 'Well it's been decided that we should try you on a course of the different drugs for TB.'

I said, 'But I thought you said I had this other long sounding name,' which I suddenly couldn't remember, although I'd only just heard it.

'Well, they seem determined that it is TB and that I'm making a mistake. We'll let you go home and have a course of these tablets. We'll keep a close eye on you and see how things go.'

There was something extremely strange about all that because Dr Mawdsley had been so positive about it being sarcoidosis and how or why he allowed his opinion to be swayed by these two chest specialists, I do not know to this day.

So home I went and had to swallow these various drugs for the treatment of TB. Two and a half months, three months went by. I began to feel weaker, my legs were worse, I began to have a cough and I felt sick quite often. I felt the tablets were upsetting me and certainly there didn't seem to be any improvement at all in the way I felt. Feeling desperate one day I phoned Dr Mawdsley's secretary, Joan Lennie, and said, 'Would you let me know when it would be convenient to have a quick word with Dr Mawdsley? Could you tell me when to phone?' She was excellent in that way and would allow me, if necessary, to speak straight to Dr Mawdsley. When I got through to him I was firm and matter of fact. I said, 'I'm just ringing up, Dr Mawdsley, to let you know that those tablets that the chest specialists insisted I take, I'm putting them all down the toilet. I don't feel any better after being on them for months. I feel much worse, I cannot go on taking them.'

'Quite right,' he said, 'quite right. What we need to do is to get you into hospital, take a few more x-rays and do one or two other tests and assess the whole situation again.'

I was expecting that I would be taken into the hospital quite quickly, but as luck would have it there was a hospital strike that spring, and in fact it was many months before I was taken into the hospital by which time my chest on x-ray was much worse, my legs were worse, everything was worse. This time Dr Mawdsley examined my neck.

'Ah yes,' he said, 'I've got it.'

'And what is it this time?'

'Well, Angela, it's a gland in your neck called the scaline gland; I was expecting to find it enlarged, and yes, it is. I want you to do something for me. I'm going to ask the two chest specialists who saw you before to come and see you individually and to examine you, and please don't mention this scaline gland or that I have been feeling for it, let alone that I have found it. Mum's the word.' And he departed.

I'd like to say that both the chest specialists were excellent people and delightful. They came in, one at a time, and to my surprise they quite quickly started feeling about on my neck, obviously knowing what they were looking for. They didn't say really anything at all and I was totally quiet.

The upshot of all of this was that it was decided to send me to the City Hospital to have a biopsy taken of this enlarged scaline gland. That didn't sound too much. I thought I'll just be sent there for the day and then back to the Northern. The day did not turn out as easily as I had expected. It's always strange to be suddenly in a different hospital. You feel out of place and that they don't want you. A bit of a pest you feel, in fact. But I had the pre-med and the operation and suddenly I was wide awake, back in the ward, and the pain in my neck was excruciating. I couldn't believe it, it was so unexpected. I thought, I've come for such a little thing, why should I be in so much pain? I called one of the nurses and said. 'Could I have something for the pain, please,' and she said, 'Oh, I'll ask Sister.'

It was quite a long wait before anyone came. I thought, I can't handle this, it was overwhelming me. And I usually have, although I say it, a pretty high pain threshold but this seemed to be beyond anything that I'd experienced.

When the Sister came she said, 'Mrs Dobbie, do try and calm down, you've just had a little biopsy and you've only got two or three stitches. I mean, don't make a fuss, most people in here have got seventy or eighty stitches.'

Well, of course, I knew that. I tried hard to persuade her that I was in agony.

She wouldn't have it. 'I'll just pull the curtains round,' she said, 'that might make you feel quieter.' I thought to myself, you mean it might shut me up.

It's amazing how acute your hearing becomes when you're desperate. I began to judge the type of walking that was going past. Was it a doctor or was it a Sister, or who was it? I did call out once or twice but nobody came inside the curtains, until after about nearly an hour the pain was reducing me, yes, reducing me really to tears. Suddenly someone popped their head round the curtain. Immediately I recognised the uniform of a Sister Tutor.

'Whatever is the matter? Mrs Dobbie, isn't it?'

'Yes,' I said, in a very stressed voice.

'Whatever is the matter?'

And it all tumbled out. 'Well, I've only had a tiny little op, I know, and I don't understand why, but I'm in such dreadful pain. I have asked for something for it but I've been told not to make a fuss.'

'Oh, but that's dreadful,' she said. 'I will go straight away and find one of the doctors.'

She came back with some painkillers for me. I could have hugged her. I felt, at last somebody with a little compassion and understanding. And I said to her, 'Why do you think there's so much pain? They've only done just a little biopsy there on my neck.'

'Ah yes,' she said, 'maybe only two or three stitches, but a lot of poking about among very sensitive nerve endings.'

'Oh, I see, I'd never thought of that.' Even the understanding of why the pain was so bad did help slightly and made me less anxious. I was more than glad to be taken back in the ambulance to the Northern.

A couple of days went by and Dr Mawdsley came back again.

'Well,' he said, 'we've got the biopsy results and it's proved it. Sarcoidosis, and that's what you have in your chest.' He explained how this neurological disease, sarcoidosis, could affect the nervous system, your chest, various glands and even joints. Amazing. I'd never heard of it. Naturally my questions were legion. What was it going to mean for me and for the future? Was it going to be so different? Dr Mawdsley explained carefully that he was sure they could clear my chest very quickly with a course of prednisalone and most likely it would be important to keep me on a maintenance dose of that forever. That, he hoped, would keep the sarcoidosis at bay. I felt a little ray of hope when he said that. Something that would stop me becoming worse. I was still confused, but somehow hopeful, optimistic. When I went home I found I wanted to tell people, 'It's not MS, it's sarcoidosis.' The trouble with that, of course, was that no one, including myself, had heard of sarcoidosis and even our own GP somehow didn't believe it. Even now, people will say and believe that I have MS. You could say, does it really matter? My answer is, yes I believe it does. Although it has meant life on steroids with all the complications that can bring, it has given me a quality of life despite increasing disability, better than I might otherwise have had. Even now I know in certain respects I have been most fortunate not to have sarcoidosis affect me in many ways that MS might have done.

Dr Mawdsley explained that he would try to find the right balance of a maintenance dose of prednisalone. I might say the steroids boost you enormously in every respect, I know it's artificial, but everything helps, and in the situation that I was in anything that helped was wonderful. For Dr Mawdsley to have been proved right was just so fantastic. There were the usual side effects of steroids. I felt I was putting on weight, but remarkably because I was as active as possible and out and about and using up a lot of energy, pushing myself about in the wheelchair and coping with tiring transfers, running the household and looking after the girls and my general activities, I didn't seem to put on as much weight as might have been expected and Dr Mawdsley used often to say, 'I give some patients five milligrams and they would be blown up like an elephant and I can give you twenty and you don't seem to have such difficulties.' That was then, of course. Even standing for a moment was a nightmare, but still, there's no doubt I did feel better.

One interesting morning which came out of this change of diagnosis was when Dr Mawdsley asked me if I would be a guinea pig, as it were, when he had to make a presentation to a group of consultants all from different faculties. They took it in turns to present an interesting case history. He said, 'I would like to present your case, Angela, but I particularly don't want you to say anything which will indicate your new diagnosis.' I fully understood that. Intriguing, it was. I had to go along to a small lecture theatre in the Royal Infirmary. I sat beside Dr Mawdsley who was at the rostrum. Gradually these twenty-eight other gentlemen came into the room. He started to present my case history. They started to fidget a bit. You could sense that they were almost switching off. However, you could see them pull themselves back to it, thinking, why would Dr Mawdsley present such a case? Multiple sclerosis is so obvious to us.

Dr Mawdsley had a style and a flair for such a presentation. He took them right to the bitter end when he said, 'Well, gentlemen, now you have the facts. There is one more piece of information I would like to give you visually. I have here Angela's chest x-rays. If any of you would like to come and look at them a little more closely, by all means do,' and he paused. After those who did get up to look closer at the x-rays returned to their seats, Dr Mawdsley continued. 'Well,' he said, 'what do you all think?'

There was then some general discussion and several people asked one or two other questions. Of course, they were all extremely brilliant in their fields and they got the message about neurological sarcoidosis. Dr Mawdsley didn't keep them much longer after that but I distinctly remember him saying to the very esteemed company that he wished to make a point which my case history highlighted. He said, 'I think it's far too often that multiple sclerosis is diagnosed without other options being considered.'

Only once in all the years since have I met someone else who had neurological sarcoidosis. For myself I felt encouraged about the change of diagnosis. It seemed there was hope for me not to go downhill as quickly as I might otherwise have done because the steroids would help and Dr Mawdsley sent me to see Dr Douglas who was a specialist in sarcoidosis. I remember him saying, 'Never let them have you on less than 10 mg daily.' As it happened I was on a lot more than that. But it gave me a quality of life that I wouldn't have had, I'm sure, which enabled me to be in the real world and continue enjoying all the activities that I had with the family and our friends. The pattern therefore became for me to have daily prednisalone, quite a large amount, 25 mg. And fortunately for me at that time I didn't suffer many of the possible side effects.

CHAPTER TWENTY-THREE

My situation was becoming much harder, not just physically: somehow that seemed the least of it. Emotionally it was beginning to affect us all more. John and the girls were magnificent in how they coped and made me feel just like any ordinary mum. But there's no doubt that the situation, as I started calling it, was affecting John and me. We didn't like to refer to it or talk about it, or even to admit openly to each other how much it was getting to us both. There came a change and it's quite scary when something you can't alter or stop can become an increasing threat in your lives but we still felt the best way to cope was to carry on as usual, and that, of course, became more difficult. In doing that, although I didn't think of it at the time, we caused more stress on ourselves. I found the most stressful time for myself was when I realised how much my disability was affecting John or the girls, or all three of them. That I found much harder to bear than the things that were difficult for me personally. I wasn't coping with my emotions about the difficulties it was creating for John and the girls. It was often raining in my heart and I squashed those feelings down. I went on doing that because it seemed the best way and I knew that if I let go I couldn't see how I'd be other than swamped.

I used to talk quite often to Connie Gibbs, our doctor. She helped a lot. I would sometimes phone her and just invite her round for a sherry and she would know that it wasn't anything really medical that I wished to speak to her about, it was more personal. She offered a wonderful outlet for my feelings and probably knew me better than anyone at that time which gave me tremendous support. I could share things with her which I didn't want to burden John with. He was already coping with so much. Not only coping with so much in ways of helping me and with the fact of the situation that we lived with all the time, but also with his own emotions which all became more difficult, more confused, and – unpleasant, I think would be the word. The feelings that are hardest are the ones which he didn't want to recognise or admit to. And, of course, those are the feelings that cause the trauma inside people.

So over these years, mid to late 70s, I think we both felt we weren't managing

so well as before. That sounds hard on ourselves. We were doing our best and
you can't do really more than that. To give a small example of how little I'd
come to terms with the situation I was living in: I found looking for new
clothes an absolute nightmare. To put something on and have to look in the
mirror – it wasn't myself or the clothes, it was me in the wheelchair. I could
hardly see the clothes because there was the wheelchair glaring me in the face,
as if my very nose were being rubbed in it. I would say I probably lasted three
or four minutes at most before I wanted to get out of the fitting room and go
home. Choosing clothes was no longer a happiness. It wasn't the fact of
choosing things that looked specially good when you're sitting down all the
time, that wasn't what was difficult. Outwardly that may seem so, and these
of course are the things you mention to others, but the truth behind all that
facade was my overwhelming feeling that if I couldn't even handle looking at
myself in the wheelchair for three minutes, how much more awful for John
and the girls who live with me all the time. Fortunately for me because I am
an outgoing person and naturally happy and enjoy being busy and sociable,
these feelings did not come to the surface all the time. But at certain times,
particularly with tiredness or stress, I was overwhelmed by them.

Fortunately I still had my central personality, my beliefs in all sorts of
things and, with regard to myself, I still believed more than ever before that
it was important to do my best in every aspect and that included my
appearance. I was lucky at that time that I wasn't putting on weight from the
steroid treatment. Sitting down all the time requires a lot of thought about
what you're going to wear. There are many things which you imagine you'll
buy, but when you put them on and you are sitting down all the time, they
just don't hang right, they don't look right, and therefore there's no point at
all in buying them. This is true for everyone, but is especially true for people
who have a physical handicap. Too often you see somebody who is not able
to think of this for themselves and those who should be doing so have not
taken the trouble. To my mind that is truly dreadful. I've always done my best
to dress as smartly as possible, and in a style which is me but which suits my
situation. I do not mean by that necessarily the type of clothing that you see
advertised for people with disabilities. One such advertisement was showing
extremely suitable and lovely clothes but at such prices they would not be
accessible to the majority of people. With a lot of care and thought, not to
mention commitment and energy, you find what you require but going round
the shops can be so difficult as the rails of clothing are far too close together.
Shoes are an absolute hell. I used to look for sensible flat shoes, which was all
I could really get on my feet, but to have boring sensible lace-up shoes at the
end of a smart outfit always seemed to me to spoil it, but I had to come to terms

with that because there wasn't any option. There must be a huge market for somebody with sensitivity and the knowledge to make footwear which can be both attractive and equally easy to put on and to take off by people with different disabilities.

This brings me to the point of the wheelchairs themselves. I was measured up properly for the wheelchair that I'd been given by the vehicle centre, but one day I was asked if I would meet a gentleman who had been in hospital recently and was now in a wheelchair. He and his wife were finding it extremely difficult to know where to get advice and how to manage. Because of my personal experience and my committee work with the Scottish Access Committee it was thought I might be able to help. The gentleman was obviously tall, but he was very thin. He was sitting in a wheelchair which was far too big for him, and he didn't even have a cushion to sit on. The footplates of that chair stuck way out in front of him and the tyres were nearly flat. In one glance I could see these problems and realise the difficulties that they were giving to this gentleman and his wife. He couldn't get round their house, they told me, because the wheelchair seemed to bump into everything. He couldn't get round much at all. They didn't realise that the tyres, not being pumped up as hard as they should be, created a difficulty, plus there was the danger of the brakes not working when the tyres were low. No one had suggested a cushion. However, before I said anything I quickly gave myself a little word, 'Go gently, don't say too much, help them to know where to get the proper help, but don't major on too many problems all at once.' They were drowning as it was.

It's all too easy for someone who has found a way to cope with different problems to make others who haven't yet found a way feel inadequate. But it was possible to tell them that the vehicle centre would enable this gentleman to have a proper wheelchair, the right size for him, which didn't have footplates sticking way out in front of him, and definitely with a cushion to sit on. I was able to mention about the tyres being pumped up and how important that was. I also asked gently about their GP, and they said, well, they hadn't really spoken to him. I advised them that he could be their friend as well as their doctor, and he could be the lifeline to so much help which is available. Whether this couple hadn't been listening to people in hospital who had tried to give them advice, I don't know. It did appear that way, but of course there's always two sides to the story. If anyone reading this has a problem which they cannot sort out, I want to assure them that there are people who can and will help. Their own doctor must be the start and there are benefits to help people which have been hard won over the years. It's ridiculous not to take them up. Pride is a very stupid and false feeling; it only trips people up.

The winters were always worse for me. It is difficult to get about in a wheelchair in the snow and if you're sitting down you get much colder than others who can run about.

I was most fortunate to be able to have the chance to travel again, and this time it was to visit my cousin David and his wife Felicity who lived at that time outside Nairobi in Kenya on an estate called Kiambu. For a long time I had longed to go there and I plucked up the courage to ring them and see if I could stay a few weeks with them during the winter. They were wonderful in agreeing that I could do that. They lived in a bungalow and thought that I would be able to manage all right, and although I was in the wheelchair I could manage a lot on my own. I knew there would be problems in Africa but that seemed to add to the excitement.

Again the rest and the heat did me so much good, and with David and Felicity's kind help I had a wonderful time despite being in a wheelchair.

As before I felt guilty though, that John, Clare and Lisa were having that awful winter at home, with a different lady this time looking after them. Not easy for them, giving me the opportunity to relax in the sunshine.

I went home feeling rested, much better in myself, and enjoying having a tan. There was, of course, much to share with the family when I got home, none of them having been to Africa. I felt ready for anything except the freezing cold and the winter which was still unrelenting.

Clare and Lisa were now ten and seven. I didn't think of it at the time but Lisa couldn't ever remember me walking and even Clare could scarcely remember, so the two of them had a mum who used a wheelchair and an adapted car. They had helped and continued to help me so much in little ways at certain difficult times. You could say, well, they were used to it, but for children anything that is different from other youngsters is always difficult, but they never made me feel that I gave them problems. They changed schools around this time, and that was not easy for either of them, especially Clare, and the fact of my disability made an added problem for her in that the school friends she'd had had grown up with me, as it were, and suddenly she had to make new friends who were faced with Clare's mum in a wheelchair.

I gave a barbecue for Clare's class. They all came and loved it and the following Monday told Clare how surprised they were that her mum was such a happy person sitting in a wheelchair.

John and I both sensed that Clare and Lisa seemed more mature than their respective peers and that has been so ever since they were quite young. I'm not wanting to make everything centre round my disability but I think it is true to say that it is definitely one of the reasons why both of them have been more sensitive, more understanding, and more grown-up than other people of their age. To give an example: one day when I'd been going to have my rest in the afternoon, and I was quite able to go from my wheelchair onto my bed and manage myself using the sliding board, stupidly I did not take the usual care and before I knew it I was on the floor. It all happened so quickly. Clare came running in, I'm sure she wasn't more than ten, and said, 'Oh Mummy, don't worry, I'll just get Lisa, we'll get you up.' Immediately I thought, definitely not. I'll get her to ring the surgery and see if one of the district nurses could call by. I'd be quite all right sitting on the floor until somebody could come. 'No, Mummy, we'll manage fine,' Clare said, 'I'll get Lisa and the two of us, I'm quite sure, can do it.'

I was not that light, not as heavy as now, that's true, thank goodness, but Clare just took over the whole situation. She moved the wheelchair away and she said to Lisa. 'Now, I want you to hold Mummy's legs, behind the knees, like a parcel,' and she said, 'We're going to turn Mummy round and I'm going to hold the top half and you're going to hold the legs, Lisa.' She explained it carefully and nicely, not in a way that made Lisa feel stupid or too little to help. Clare was encouraging with her words, most encouraging. In between she would say to me, 'Now don't worry, Mummy, it'll be all right.' Before I knew it, they'd turned me around on the floor, and then Clare said to Lisa, 'Now, when I say three, we're going to lift Mummy together onto the bed,' which was exactly what happened. Full marks, girls, I couldn't believe it. It was all over in a few minutes. I remember thinking at the time that it was as if Clare had had some nursing training. Not only did she know what to do, but also the way she took control, she didn't panic in any way. Ten is not very grown-up to deal with a situation like that so well. I felt mightily proud of both of them.

I was determined that our family, John, Clare, Lisa and myself, could enjoy all the things that other families did and I suppose because of my underlying concern of holding them back, or causing them problems through my disability, I made considerable, sometimes enormous, efforts. I always had their friends to stay and made them feel free to join in with everything and never, never, were they to feel that they would have to say, no, they couldn't manage because they had to help Mummy. One person in the family with a disability is more than enough. I think it's quite sad really when the next generation are held back, shut in, and have to turn down opportunities because they have to cope with the support for a person like myself. I don't mean that they shouldn't help in any way, of course, I don't mean that, but I do mean that their lives should not be touched more than is absolutely necessary, and that they should know and experience the freedom which as individual people they're entitled to. I remember thinking over the years quite often, we're only in this world once, and it's their turn now.

We were indeed a very busy household and a happy one too. But it's true that I couldn't have managed all that we did if I hadn't had a considerable amount of help. I increased the amount of help I had in the mornings and also kept on with excellent young people in the afternoons, and then one day Dr Gibbs said, 'Why don't you have someone on a Saturday, Angela?' I thought that was overdoing it a bit. 'No,' she said, 'after all, the family are busy, John with golf and the girls with their friends; you could do more yourself on a Saturday.'

I very much liked the idea of that because Saturdays, though I tried not to show it, had become rather boring and even lonely. I welcomed the thought of going out on a Saturday, with someone to help me, which I needed now. I was definitely not managing so well in myself, emotionally, I mean. I was coming to a time which, of course, crept up on me gradually, when I didn't feel myself at all and often didn't behave like myself at all, more stress for the girls, definitely, and John in particular. It was all very well me going off to Australia and enjoying the sunshine, and Kenya more recently, which had done me a lot of good, but I did feel guilty about all that, and then I began to think, what about us all going together? It had long been a sadness for me that I couldn't share with them all my Australian life and all my experiences and wonderful family out there.

When I latch on to an idea like that it seems to pick up speed, like the Inter City train, and before I know it I have more than an idea, it becomes a plan. When I suggested it to John, he said, 'Oh, that's ridiculous. I mean it's far too expensive, and we couldn't possibly all four of us go. I think it's too much, Angela.'

But I made the point that I had some money in the building society and it seemed a wonderful way of using it, for all four of us to have a holiday in Australia that we could share forever. To do it then when the children were young would be wise, because when they grew up they would wish to travel with their own age group. I won John over to it.

We both felt also that the girls had been so marvellous in coping with the new school situation which we had imposed upon them and in making new friends. They deserved a real treat, something special, so we started to plan to go to Australia in the girls' summer holidays. I said to John, 'It's no good going for a short time, it's too far, you'll have to get some extra time off from the business.'

He said, 'Well, I couldn't possibly take eight weeks; maybe I could squeeze five, it would be unfair to take more.'

We then broke the news to the girls who, of course, were ecstatic. Next we planned where we'd like to go and what we'd like to see. We must see the Barrier Reef, what about seeing Ayer's Rock? 'Hang on a minute,' said John, 'we can't see everything, we certainly can't afford to do everything; you'll have to decide especially what you'd like to do.' And then he'd say, 'Don't you think it would be rather too much having all four of us to stay anywhere?' I know that's true, but knowing wonderful families in Australia I somehow felt it would be all right.

I could hardly wait to get to the end of the summer term but the holidays came at last and we were off. Edinburgh to London, London to Sydney. The flight was fairly uneventful. Some of us slept a little bit. John has an amazing capacity to relax and sleep a bit, and is very self-contained on a journey. The girls were a bit fidgety. Clare finds it difficult to sleep on a flight, and so do I. Lisa managed it better, but she discovered that she had quite a problem with her ears. Each time we landed it was painful for her. But eventually there we were, all four of us, arriving in Sydney and going to stay with my sister Mary and family. So fantastic of them to have all four of us! We needed more than one car, of course, with four of us and golf clubs, wheelchair, and far too much luggage. However, before we got to the cars, there was no sign at all of Clare's case. Qantas were excellent though and they said they'd pay about $250 immediately for us to go out and kit her out with the basics. My sister Mary took her up to the local High Street. I think Clare was pleased to choose all these new Australian clothes; they seemed much more fun than the choice back home in Scotland.

After about ten days in Sydney we were going to Hayman Island on the Barrier Reef. It had taken a lot of careful research and thinking back home to decide on that. After that we were going to return to Sydney for a little while longer before going down to Melbourne where John's Aunt Betty and family stayed. Tremendous excitement at the thought of going to the Barrier Reef! It was something I had always wanted to do, and now I was able to share it with John and the girls. We flew from Sydney up to Brisbane, and then we had to get into a small plane to go to Rockhampton and there we changed into a huge helicopter. It sounds exciting to go in a helicopter, but my experience of it was awful. It's true we could see the coral wonderfully as we flew low across the Reef and that was spectacular, but I must say the noise was terrible. Then we landed at Hayman Island. You could say, it has been commercialised, while Green Island or Heron and some of the others are totally unspoilt, but we'd chosen Hayman Island because we'd found out that there would be activity and fun there for all four of us, who might wish to enjoy different things at different times. Another appealing thing was that there was a little train, like a toy train, which took you from the jetty along to the hotel.

The hotel was a series of low buildings with a large swimming pool in the centre, beautiful gardens, and right along the shore of the beach there was a lawn between the sand and a row of chalets. We'd booked two of these. There were little paths which led all the way round so there was no problem of access for me. We sank into the beauty of that place. The girls had absolute freedom to run around and do what they wanted. There were plenty of other children. They could run straight out of their cabin, just a few yards across the grass, onto the beach and into that wonderful warm, azure blue water. Every day on the island John and I had breakfast brought to our chalet and we'd sit on our little verandah, overlooking this fabulous beach and the water. You didn't feel as if there were other people around, as you ate those breakfasts of delicious tropical fruit and hot croissants.

We'd heard you could take a boat out to a small atoll off our island. We thought that would be fun. It was all arranged and we'd asked the hotel to give us a picnic. We went along to the jetty and waited for the man to bring the boat round to the side of it. We'd got rather a lot of things: the picnic itself, snorkelling gear, flippers, towels, etc. We'd hardly been on the jetty a moment when I looked down at the water with dismay. The boats were way, way down low. The tide was out. It had never crossed our minds to check on something

John, Clare and Lisa on Hayman Island, Barrier Reef

145

like that. There we were, all ready, and so excited to go on this fabulous all-day picnic, just the four of us to our own little island, as we were already calling it, but how on earth was somebody like myself going to get down those tiny little steps into the boat. As John looked at it, he said, 'I think that is our boat,' upon which the boatman himself came along. He didn't look very young or able. I didn't think it would be suitable to ask him to help me, and I had visions in that moment of John and the girls going and myself having to stay behind. But no, something wonderful happened next. A large steamer came into the jetty and off it poured masses of visitors to the island. At the front of this group of people was a giant of a man – he must have been at least 6'6" with the broadest shoulders and largest muscles that I have ever seen. Instantly I thought, this is the person, I must ask him. I didn't hold back for a moment. I went straight up to him and said, 'Excuse me, could you possibly give me some help?'

'Yes,' he said, 'of course, if I can.'

I explained the need for someone to help me down those awful steps into the boat.

'Oh, not a problem at all,' he said.

With that, he picked me up as if I were a feather, which indeed I was not, and he seemed, despite his size and weight, to dance down those narrow little steps and placed me gently in the boat. It was all over in a moment, I couldn't believe it. 'Thank you,' I said, 'it's given me such happiness to know I can go on this trip today, thank you very much.' John and the girls joined me down in the boat and the boatman gave John a few instructions about the outboard motor. We set off, full of excitement, round the end of the jetty and we could see our little island just in the distance, not too far away.

It was a fabulous day, as every day was up there. The sparkling blue and warmth of that water beckoned your fingers to trail in it. I did that all the time. My obsession for water never left me. I was sitting in the middle of the boat. Clare was up at the bow, and John was sitting with Lisa in the stern steering the boat. Everything seemed to be going fine, but after about four minutes there was a terrible crunch and we came to a halt. Whatever was that? Suddenly Clare was shouting from the bow of the boat, 'Daddy, Daddy, I can see the bottom, I can see all the coral.'

That was it, of course, the coral, we had to be stuck on that. In the beginning we'd been in the channel for the big steamers but we didn't remember anyone saying that we should steer a particular course. Clare seemed hysterical, jumping up and down; in fact, at one stage she was about to jump out.

John said, 'Clare, sit down, you mustn't do that, you might land on some spiky bit of coral and cut your feet; you've all got to calm down.' Personally,

I felt it was quite a serious situation but, as mothers have to, I hid those feelings, calmed the girls down, and we decided to change places. John put me in the bow of the boat and the girls in the middle, while he stayed in charge of the outboard motor. First of all, John would have to try and push us off the coral with the oar and hopefully he would manage it. It took quite some time and with each movement and grinding noise I was thinking about the bottom of the boat, which didn't belong to us. We came free from the reef, what a relief! I then had the responsibility of staring down into the water and trying to advise John about the depth of the water we were going through. Nightmare.

The fact that we could be stuck again concentrated my mind and I tried not to be distracted by the myriads of fish and colours of the coral. We did eventually reach the wonderful white beach of this tiny island, safely. We just ran the boat up onto the sand. There was absolute silence apart from the lapping of that clear turquoise water. Yes, we thought, this is our island. It was very hot. We didn't have any shade, there wasn't a single tree, but we didn't mind, we had lots of sun cream, sun glasses, and the girls were in the water most of the time. We all seemed quite hungry. The hotel had made us a delicious picnic. It was special for just the four of us to be on that tiny atoll with no one else in the whole world there, and it is difficult to explain what a wonderful feeling that was. The girls were keen to go snorkelling, but I was not at all interested. I'm not keen on being under the water. I loved to be on the water, and in it, but not ever under it. In fact, by this time I was feeling quite tired and I said to the family, 'Well you go off, and that's fine, explore the coral with your snorkels and I'll just stay here.'

John suddenly said, 'What about the tide? It's coming in now. We'd better bring you up the beach a bit, Angela, we don't want you dozing on the rug there under your sun hat with the water suddenly lapping up to your knees.'

No, I thought, not too good, that, very wise of him to think ahead of these things. It hadn't crossed my mind. They kindly got me settled and off the three of them went with their snorkels and their flippers. Every now and again one of them would come running up the beach to say, 'Oh, Mum, Angela, we've seen this amazing coral,' and they kept talking about the wonderful shoals of different coloured fish. It all sounded brilliant. I wasn't unhappy that I wasn't doing what they were doing. I was sharing their happiness and it was just fine.

After our wonderful time on Hayman Island we went to stay with John's relations in Melbourne, his Aunt Betty Mackay and her family. To have all four of us to stay was marvellous of them. I seemed to get a bit tired and over-emotional about things while I was there. Not that I thought about it in particular at the time, but looking back, I remember that I did.

Then we had to say a sad goodbye to John and he flew back to Scotland.

The girls and I were going to my cousin Helen and her husband John's sheep station. I would have given anything for John to come with us to share that: it was one of my most favourite places.

We flew from Melbourne in a Focker Friendship. The girls were so excited; they couldn't believe how tiny it was compared to the enormous Jumbo jet we'd flown in from London. I was wondering how we'd all fit in, plus luggage, not to mention the wheelchair, even though it did fold up quite neatly. The young pilot jumped out and soon stowed away the baggage and said to the girls, 'Now, if you'd like to sit near me in front I think we'll put Mum in this rear seat; we'll lift her up and back her in,' which is what they virtually did. Then they put the wheelchair in beside me and the girls got in another tiny door next to the cockpit. Inside the plane was already a young lad of about seventeen who was returning to his family's sheep station. That was the total capacity of this plane; the pilot, the young lad, Clare and Lisa, and myself. There was no room for another person or another piece of luggage.

Helen and John met us at Griffith. The girls were full of questions. The land looked parched. We couldn't imagine what the sheep ate. But John was telling us that not easily seen to the eyes, especially not while travelling along, there are little burrs in the soil which have nine prickles on them and each prickle contains all the different vitamins and nutrients that the sheep need, and that's how they survive in such arid land. Everything was so flat. The horizon, John said, was seven miles, which gives you an idea of the distance.

That first evening John Sides had the most wonderful news for all three of us which was that while we were there, the shearing team were coming to shear the entire head of sheep. The girls thought that this was fabulous and it was a very long time since I had seen sheep being sheared, in fact way back when I was little on my uncle's sheep station.

When the shearers arrived we soon discovered the tremendous characters they were, and they much enjoyed teasing the girls and joking with them and telling them funny stories. The girls understood that while we were in the country, as indeed wherever we were, it was important to fit in with whatever was going on, and also to be helpful wherever possible. This particular morning we were all down watching the shearing. One of the shearers said to Clare, would she go up to the house to get the smoko? Well, off she went but she seemed to be taking ages and the men became rather fed-up. I didn't know what the smoko was, and I didn't really think about it. Meanwhile Clare back at the house was thinking smoko was something like Omo washing detergent and was looking around in the laundry for something like that, whereas what it really meant was the morning tea-time and Helen had boxes already packed with flasks of tea and lovely home-made cookies. Eventually, of course, somebody else went up and told her what she should have been looking for, and when she came back to the shearing shed they gave her the most awful ribbing. Another day the girls were adventurous enough to turn the hose on these chaps. Well, that was not a good idea. They had a drenching the other way round in return.

Unfortunately, while we were there the girls saw a twelve-foot brown snake. Revolting. I just find snakes revolting, and I think I've passed on my revulsion to the girls, which is a bad thing to do, but I got it from my mother and I think it's something which just goes down through our family. We always took care to empty our boots and shoes before putting them on. Everyone thinks about spiders being horrible, and there are some dangerous ones, although in fact the largest ones of all are the least dangerous.

Far too soon the day came when we had to fly back to Sydney. Helen was driving us to Griffith Airport when we had a most frightening experience. A flock of gallahs, which are large white birds, came crashing into the windscreen, completely blinding her. She pulled up quickly; the windscreen was disgustingly splattered. The girls were horrified and upset. Helen stayed wonderfully calm. It does happen up here but, thank goodness, not too often, she said. It spoilt that trip to the airport, but again it is something which has to be accepted in the country. Back to Sydney, and to stay the last week with my sister and family and to see as much of family and friends as we could. I realised that we were going to have excess luggage because the case that Qantas had lost on the way out to Sydney had been found three weeks later. By that time, of course, we had used the money they had given us to buy Clare new clothes, new suitcase, new everything really. Happily, though, Qantas gave me a letter which explained our excess luggage since it had been their fault. I was to be glad of that letter.

I knew that I would have to have a catheter for the journey because it's too difficult when you can't walk to get to the loo. This had worked fine on the flight out, and so Jan Dowling, a Nursing Sister and friend of Mary's, did the catheterisation the night before we left for London. It was not very pleasant, but was something I had to have done or I wouldn't have been able to make the journey. Our flight out from Sydney wasn't until the following evening and we'd been invited to Clareville, on Pitwater, for lunch and my cousin Freddie was going to take us to the airport in the evening from there. We went down with all our luggage and me in the wheelchair. It fairly adds up, but I wasn't worrying at that stage about it. After lunch Freddie said, 'How about us all going out in the yacht before you leave, we've got plenty of time. Who would like to come?' Of course the girls shouted, 'Yes please.' And I rather gingerly put up my hand, thinking there would probably be too many in the boat and anyway it would be such a hassle getting me in and out of it.

'No, not at all,' said Freddie, 'not a bother. There's plenty of us to help you and there's plenty of room in the boat.'

He knew how much I loved it. This seemed definitely the icing on the cake. They took me down those steep steps to the beach and got me into the boat. Several of the family came with us and we had a brilliant sail for about an hour and a half. Everything went well and was fine, and we came up to the house quite a while later feeling full of the sun and salt air.

Finally, we were all packed into Freddie's large estate car, driving to Mascot Airport. The day was still lovely. It's true I was a little tired, but everything seemed just fine until, after about twenty minutes, I thought, oh dear, something's wrong. The right leg of my trousers felt wet. I thought, oh well, it's probably just because they're wet from being out in the boat. I quickly realised it was nothing of the kind. There was something drastically wrong with the leg bag from the catheter. I said to Freddie as he drove us along. 'We'll need to go into the nearest hospital on the way, Freddie, I'm going to need to get some more equipment.' Stupidly, I had not counted carefully how much I'd need and, being very inexperienced in these matters, I hadn't an extra leg bag to use.

'Don't worry,' said Freddie, 'we'll pass several hospitals. We'll go into the first one we come to.'

When we asked them, they said they had no such thing as equipment that would help me. I couldn't believe it. 'That kind of nursing equipment you get from a chemist,' they said. It was Sunday and nothing like that would be open. I thought, this is serious. I have a long journey ahead of me, what am I going to do? A totally new situation, flung on my own resources, nobody to advise me.

I've no idea what made me think of it but when we got to the second hospital and they said they didn't have anything either that was suitable, I said, 'Well, do you have some plastic bags and elastic bands, could you manage that?'

They looked at me rather sideways and said, 'Well, yes, I think we could manage that. Whatever are you going to do with them?'

I said, 'If I can't have a leg bag to go on the end of this catheter which I've got to have in maybe I could try a plastic bag, like a freezer bag, and we could attach it to the end of the catheter with an elastic band.'

'What a good idea,' they said, 'I suppose it might work.'

That is how I managed all the way from Sydney to Edinburgh. Not easy, but miraculously I managed it, taking care of course that we changed the bag frequently, and Clare was such an excellent help to me in doing that.

When we came to the airport, we went up to the desk, myself in the wheelchair of course, the girls again trailing along their Australiana bags which by this time were packed full, with koala bears on top. The bags seemed so heavy; the girls were tired and not looking forward to the flight. As we approached the desk with the tickets a tall Qantas man peered down at me over the desk. We were quite a sight I suppose. A mother in a wheelchair, two daughters, hats, bags, koala bears, far too much luggage, a heap, you could say, in front of him. Quickly I remembered the letter from Qantas and passed it up to him. 'I think this will help to explain the situation,' I said. He made no comment but read the letter quickly.

'I see,' he said, 'lucky you having this letter, very lucky. Given the situation, we'll just have to stow you all away somewhere.'

It was a good flight except that I do get cramp, not being able to get up and walk about like everybody else. The worst bit is when they dim the lights and everyone appears to be sleeping; the cramp gets worse and the painkillers don't seem to help at all. But I found the stewardess was excellent and she moved my legs for me which improved the circulation. Tremendous help, that, in fact far more effective than painkillers.

We were due to arrive in London early in the morning, and we'd planned to go up on the Shuttle. I was looking forward to arriving in Edinburgh with John meeting us, probably at about ten o'clock in the morning. It was not to be. We went straight across to the British Airways terminal and were confront-ed with an attitude problem which nothing seemed to shift. I did understand that two children, mother in a wheelchair and the vast amount of luggage that we had was not a welcome sight at the check-in desk to the early morning Shuttle, normally taking smart businessmen to Edinburgh to their various meetings. I more than understood that, and said to the girls, 'We'll have some breakfast here and get on the next flight.' The British Airways stewardess started calling the next flight and didn't seem to indicate to us that we were going to be part of it and said in reply to my question of 'what about us?' 'Oh, I'm sorry, Mrs Dobbie, we can't possibly take you on this flight either.'

I said, 'Why ever not? We've been here long enough now surely to be entitled to a place.'

'Well, yes, that's true,' she said, 'but the problem is that we haven't got anybody to take you on board.'

I said, 'Whatever do you mean? You have so many staff and I have recently been on and off aeroplanes many times. I've just come all the way from Sydney, and you're now telling me that you will not or cannot find a way of taking me on board this Shuttle flight to Edinburgh. Could you explain that?' She looked somewhat embarrassed, to be honest.

I said, 'What is the problem?'

'Well,' she continued, 'there is a dispute at the moment about who will help disabled people to get on and off flights.'

After the long journey, and things which could have been difficult having been smoothed so much on the holiday by wonderful family and friends, and also by the different airways that we'd been on in Australia, I found this totally unacceptable.

'I'm afraid,' said the stewardess, 'you'll have to wait until the afternoon flight.'

I said, 'But what good it that? Who is going to change their mind and take me on board that flight?'

By this time the girls, particularly Clare, were upset, and I myself was feeling not only angry but also distressed, that our holiday should end like this, and that instead of being at home in Edinburgh, we were still stuck at Heathrow. There seemed nothing we could do at that moment but somehow the stewardess did reassure me that they would definitely place us on the afternoon flight.

At this particular point, Clare had had it. She said, 'Mummy I'm just going to look at those books over there.' Stupidly, I wasn't quick enough to realise she had something else in mind. I was reading Lisa a story to try and help pass the time, and when I looked up to see Clare at the bookstand, to my horror, there wasn't a sight of her, not anywhere at all. I went round the waiting area, not a sign of Clare. Suddenly I thought of the stories you hear of children going off with someone. I didn't in fact believe Clare was that kind of child, because at eleven she was much more sensible. But I was worried she'd get lost in the busy airport concourse. The only thing to do was to ask them to put on the Tannoy, would Clare Dobbie please come back to the Shuttle lounge of British Airways, and if anyone saw a young person with her description which I gave, with her lovely fair auburn hair, sun-tan, dressed in a cream Hayman Island sweatshirt, would they please bring her to the British Airways shuttle lounge. It wasn't long, although it seemed ages, that Clare herself returned with a tear-stained face to join Lisa and me, who were not feeling much better ourselves.

It was such a long and boring wait. The afternoon came. In fact, it was the captain of the flight and one of the stewards who helped me onto that aeroplane which enabled us to complete our journey. A pity to end a wonderful trip like that. I was angry to the point of writing to the Chairman of the British Airport Authority and had an excellent letter back, apologising for our awful experience, and explaining that indeed there was a dispute, but that it was being resolved by employing paramedics, all of which was eminently sensible but unfortunately too late for the girls and myself.

CHAPTER TWENTY-FOUR

Returning home can be as exciting as going away. The girls returned to school immediately and I was quickly back into running the house and all my usual activities, including Access work. I had learned a lot about how to cope with my disability while away about how to travel, but somehow during those months after we returned I didn't feel myself. I felt down and irritable. I didn't recognise it as being depressed. When I saw Dr Mawdsley next I explained these feelings to him and he said, 'Angela, I think the problem is that you have got here a depressive illness and it's not anything to do with your general situation.' I found that impossible to believe, absolutely impossible to believe, and I said, 'But surely the fact that I can't taste things properly and about this business of noise?' I couldn't see, I didn't understand or if I could and did, I didn't want to understand that depression was the cause of these problems. I saw him quite a lot. Dr Mawdsley did his best to persuade me and said, 'In fact, Angela, I can't help you until you will let me do so.'

During the next nine months I became much worse. I felt my hands definitely numb and could hardly taste anything. Even normal sound often made me feel that a knitting needle was going through my head from ear to ear. I felt edgy very quickly and not able to cope with what was going on around me. I was very unlike myself, and yet for all that time I would not believe what Dr Mawdsley was telling me. I wouldn't accept it. As those months went on it must have been a nightmare for John, Clare and Lisa because when you're like that it somehow makes you quite aggressive which, I think it's fair to say, isn't generally part of my nature at all. I remember one awful incident in the kitchen when I was sitting by the sink in my wheelchair and I've no idea what the problem was, but I remember feeling sharply angry and turning round in my chair so quickly, that I hurt one of them badly on the leg with the footplates. It seemed such an aggressive way to behave and everyone was shocked, including myself, and yet the weeks came and went and the months went by and I seemed to carry on as usual. John and the girls were marvellous but they were now coping with not only Mum in a wheelchair but also Mum who was not herself, Mum who over-reacted and became aggressive and kept asking for the radio to be turned down, or anything to be turned down, or people to be quiet.

Fortunately the day came which I shall not forget. I was sitting alone and I've no idea why it was that particular moment, but in my heart I knew that if I didn't get help from Dr Mawdsley, I was never going to be me again. That was my exact thinking at that time. It was good John was at home. I told him what I felt. He couldn't wait to go to the telephone and phone Dr Mawdsley who quickly gave me an appointment. How fortunate I was to have this excellent neurologist to look after me, and to think of all those months, nearly nine months, that I had resisted his expertise.

When I did see him he said, 'I know it's all part of the problem, Angela, that you didn't believe me, but let's not dwell on that, let's go forward. I think we ought to try you on some anti-depressant tablets. They may make you put on weight and give you one or two little side effects, but I think we ought to try them and just take it from there.' I was prepared now to do whatever he said. I was by this time feeling desperate. I took the pills for quite a long time. I understood it would be at least three weeks before I could expect any improvement from them. But to my disappointment, and Dr Mawdsley's also, they didn't seem to have any effect on me at all, so that meant more weeks and months went by, and I was becoming less and less like myself. By now I couldn't sleep, hardly at all. Even though I took sleeping tablets I would wake up an hour after taking them and what a long night that meant. So on top of being unwell in the ways I've mentioned, I became exhausted.

Dr Mawdsley decided to stop the tablets and said that I ought to see a psychiatrist. To be honest, when he told me that, I thought, well, this is definitely the end of the road, Angela. Even though I know what excellent work they do, to be told that you need to go and see a psychiatrist just seemed to me that I had gone a long way down. Frightened, I think, would cover my feelings about it, but at the same time I didn't resist. I didn't really care where I was very much. Dr Mawdsley said, 'Now, I want you to be seen by this psychiatrist, Dr Lloyd, as an in-patient in the Royal Infirmary.' I can honestly say I was glad to go into the hospital. Strange to say, that. I just lay in my bed, I still couldn't sleep, but I felt somehow there were many people about to take care of everything and that I didn't need to worry or think about anyone, even myself.

The senior registrar came to talk to me about different things and, of course, to give me a neurological examination, which I was more than used to by now. He said, 'Now, we have a problem, Angela, in that Dr Lloyd unfortunately is not at all well. He has serious 'flu and there's no possibility of him seeing you for probably about a week, or maybe longer.' Even that didn't seem to cause me worry. He said, 'I'm going to fix it though that you can be seen by someone else,' and neither did that seem to bother me. But the following day when Dr Mawdsley came on his rounds and the registrar told him how he'd arranged for me to be seen by a different psychiatrist, Dr Mawdsley's fury was unbelievable. He said, 'I've brought Angela into the Royal here to be seen by Dr Lloyd, and I don't care how long she waits, it'll probably do her good just to lie in bed and get up when she feels like it, to be rested and have some space and time. She will wait here for Dr Lloyd to get better.' The other doctors were amazed. I felt sorry for the registrar who had only been trying to do his best.

A week later the day came when I met Dr Lloyd, and I would like to say he was well worth waiting for. I was extremely nervous of talking to anyone like that. I had no idea what to expect so I don't know what I was nervous of, but I was. I had no confidence at all; I had nothing really. I didn't feel much at all about anything. I was to see him in a room off the ward and when I went along in my wheelchair and went into the room he stood up and extended his hand to introduce himself. I was completely bowled over by the fact that he looked exactly like Richard Stevenson, the younger brother of our best man, Sam. It completely overtook that first session with Dr Lloyd, in fact so much so that I had to mention it to him, and talk about it, to get past it, because I had a real problem in that anything I was going to say to this doctor would be like talking to Richard Stevenson, which would hardly have been suitable.

I saw Dr Lloyd regularly, every second day while I was in the hospital for two weeks, and then he let me go home on my birthday, 23rd October. This time he changed my sleeping pills by putting them up dramatically, and I was now getting some sleep. I was on no anti-depressants at all and he said, 'What we'll need to do is to continue these sessions with you as an out-patient.' I was more than glad that I was in the hospital for those early sessions. They were harrowing. How did he do it, what did he do, what did he ask me? He took me back to the beginning, to that dreadful day when John was given the job of telling me that I had MS. And then he took me through all the years since then, and he made me face all the things that I had buried in my sub-conscious, emotions I had been pushing down, which I had refused to allow to come to the surface. It was a nightmare, it was so upsetting. I always felt completely drained out after each session, but at all times I felt Dr Lloyd was in control in his special quiet way. I was constantly surprised at the things that we talked of which I had long since forgotten. Hurtful things and difficult emotions that I'd had about my disability, and my concerns and fear of it affecting our marriage. Problems which I tried to help other people with, not realising that doing that was having a bad effect on myself. There were many difficulties about which Dr Lloyd would open up an avenue of thought which I never dreamt of mentioning to him. Indeed, if I went with an idea in my mind of what I felt I should discuss with him in a particular session, somehow it never was that which came out. He'd always find something else more important that needed pulling out of my sub-conscious that I needed to face and discuss with him, in order to get rid of it. I was most fortunate that when I came out of each of those sessions as an out-patient my wonderful friend Diana Mackay was always there to pick me up, not only to help me into the car with my wheelchair, but also to pick me up generally and, being the marvellous friend that she is, she was never intrusive in any way about what I'd been going through. It didn't matter how much of a state I was in when she collected me, she gave me that time on the journey home to get myself together.

On reflection then, over the past eighteen months that I've just described, I was in a constant battle, losing most of the time, but nevertheless still fighting but unfortunately the problems in my mind continued. For John, Clare and Lisa those eighteen months, and even the years after that, must have been very, very hard. We all carried on as usual, as I've said before. It seemed the best way to handle our situation. With hindsight, I wonder. But I know in my heart I wouldn't have had it any other way, in that I wanted to be active for as long as I could. I was by this time fighting a battle to stand up at all. My legs were much weaker and with that came the prospect of being less independent, whether getting in and out of bed or managing in the bathroom. I can say that in one sentence, but it covers so much emotion in myself, that one sentence cannot convey my feelings on this.

With very great difficulty I was still managing on my own in the bathroom, except for having a bath, but when I told Dr Mawdsley about how I stood up leaning on the basin to give me two hands free, and then turned around on to the loo, he said, 'I don't want to hear about it, Angela. As far as I'm concerned you can't stand up and you don't stand up. It sounds highly dangerous to me.' He was right, of course, but I knew that the moment I needed help with these personal issues, so much was going to change for me. It wasn't the help from other people that I minded, I had a home help every morning and someone in the afternoons. I didn't mind them helping me. But I couldn't bear the thought of being more of a burden on John by needing him to help me with all the personal things. It wasn't that I didn't want him to help me but I didn't want it for him, that he would be burdened with it. That was what kept me going, trying harder and harder, and it is amazing how much you can continue to do. So in many ways you could say, 'Well, that was a good thing, Angela,' and so I told myself. But in reality I was pushing myself towards a precipice and very nearly over it. I realised that probably one day the legs would just give way completely and I would have a horrible fall, then I would just be more bother. And also I was still not out of my emotional nightmare. I continued to see Dr Lloyd, and had improved, but despite his excellent care I was still far from being myself and far from being Angela to John and Mum to the girls.

After Christmas when the girls were thirteen and ten I flew again to Sydney, once again my sister Mary and family being most generous in having me. In recent months we'd noticed quite a difference in Mary's letters, not that she writes often, but we'd noticed that their preoccupation with Amway had given way to something else and what the something else was we weren't quite sure, except that in any letters we did receive Mary was always mentioning what wonderful people they'd met at a new church they went to and how they were all feeling so happy. We didn't have any idea of what she and Michael had become involved in. The only thing I knew immediately was that they seemed far more relaxed, definitely happy, and yes, somehow different. I was soon to find out why. Very shortly after my arrival which was at New Year, and of course a hot one rather than a cold Scottish Hogmanay, Mary said they were going to a special service at their church and she hoped very much that I would go with them. I said, 'What kind of service is it, Mary, and what kind of church is it that you're going to now?'

'Oh,' she said, 'you'll see when we get there. It's quite different to where we were before and we've met such wonderful people,' and she swept on in that vein, so excited and looking forward to sharing with me all the new things that were happening in their lives. I wasn't over my jet lag and I wasn't highly receptive in any way to all this constant talk about church and different people, and certainly I felt wary about this service because Mary did describe it as a healing service. I hadn't a clue what it would be like. I'd never been to any such thing.

I didn't have much option, in fact none at all, but to go with them to this service which meant having a meal with about eight hundred other people, very well organised, and then we were to listen to an evangelist called Pastor Gordon Gibbs who Mary said had a healing ministry. I suppose I was intrigued and I enjoyed listening and I was delighted to see Mary and Michael and the children so happy, but I definitely didn't want to be involved. We were in the front row, myself in my wheelchair in a space, my sister Mary on one side and Michael on the other. Quickly I realised that this was going to be a totally different experience. Pastor Gibbs spoke in a way which challenged people from the floor to come forward. He said, 'I know there's somebody here who has a particular kind of headache,' and he would describe it in considerable detail, and then ask them to come forward. 'We can heal that and have them be free of it.' In my heart I was thinking, what a lot of hocus pocus, I certainly don't believe this rubbish, but to my amazement people did go forward. People would stand there right in front of us and the Pastor and others would lay their hands on the person's shoulders and their head, and then to my horror the person would fall down. I thought, there's something wrong about this, I don't like it, I don't like it at all, and I was so surprised that Mary and Michael would be involved with anything like that.

It was a hot night; the pain I'd had for months in my right leg was killing me. I'd had my tablets, so I certainly couldn't have any more for another four hours which seemed an eternity away. To my horror this Pastor started to describe a pain which went down the back of a person's right leg and under their heel and right under their foot. I could hardly bear to breathe. It was an exact description of the pain I was in. There must be lots of people, I thought, with pain like that, there's bound to be lots of people who will go forward. Nobody, nobody went forward. I looked straight ahead, I tried to breathe normally. I did not want to catch my sister's eye. They, of course, she and Michael, had no idea what I was thinking or any knowledge of the pain which I was suffering. Throughout the time that the evangelist stood there and healed many people, he came back at least four times to describe the pain that I was in, and towards the end he said, 'I realise whoever has this problem doesn't wish to come forward. I more than understand, but please make sure you speak to me at the end, just quietly. I would like to help you, I know I can help you.'

I wanted nothing to do with this; I couldn't wait for the end, I couldn't wait to go home and to be away from it all, but going out of the door saying goodnight to this excellent man with kind eyes, I felt that he knew it was me, but he made no comment and neither did I.

I didn't believe it and I didn't want anyone to make my leg better for only a short while for the pain just to come back again. It would have to be faced, the hell of it, I knew. I absolutely did not believe that people could be healed in any way like that. I didn't say anything to Mary and Michael; I kept this to myself for quite a while. But I quickly realised that even if I didn't want to be involved, living with them in their home as I was, I couldn't help but be so.

At this time Mary and Michael were fostering a little girl, Danielle, so they were now five, and had also given part of their home to a family, Jan and Neil Dowling and their three children. This had come about because Neil, who'd been a grazier, had had an extraordinary experience one night while his wife had been on night duty as a nursing Sister, an experience which took him from his bed to his knees on the floor asking a Lord that he didn't or hadn't believed in, to help him. It's a wonderful story, a tremendous witness. It's his story and not mine but it was dramatic and even Jan, who'd been a Christian for a long time, couldn't believe it when she came home in the morning and found Neil walking round their home singing hymns and speaking passages out of the Bible which he'd never read in his life. I need to tell you just that hint of it all to give you some background to the fact that he gave up his position managing the family property and came to Sydney to go to Bible College. They had nothing and nowhere to go. Jan could do her nursing and that would bring some income, but they had three children to support. Mary and Michael were able to offer them the hospitality of their home by extending it out at the back making a large family room. So there we were, eleven of us under one roof in that hot summer in Sydney, an amazing experience. It wasn't easy, it had its flash moments, but I was privileged to be there at that time. Maybe I was meant to be there. What could I do to help in such a large household? Well, I quickly learned that come five in the evening, mums are tired and have had it, children are also hot, so I would take the littlies onto the verandah and read them stories while Jan and Mary would prepare their supper. I couldn't help but absorb the happiness of these two families, their calm self control, and was impressed by their total belief in Jesus. More than that, each of them talked about allowing Jesus to come into their lives and to be in charge of them. Now all this was far too much for me to take in although I had always taken going to church seriously. My first feeling was that I didn't want anyone else to be in charge of my life; we'd all been brought up to be so independent.

Neil was the one I pestered with questions and with every question I asked, his answer would make me ask more questions. One afternoon when we were quietly talking together he said, 'Angela, one day you will stop asking questions, you will realise that we don't have to understand everything and you will totally believe that the Lord Jesus reigns, and if you will allow him he will come and reign in your heart and be in control of you, but only if you ask him to do so.'

I couldn't handle all this, I didn't want to handle it, my mind was going in all directions. Most of what I'd understood of church and Christianity was somehow a pale shadow of what these lovely people were showing me.

I went to many services at their church, which I came to enjoy really, especially the singing, but when it came to their pastor speaking, although they were always good sermons the delivery was, I thought, very American in style and Phil Pringle, the pastor, had this way of saying the same sentence over and over again. This irritated me, as if we couldn't get the message the first time. I'm not sure if it irritated others, but it certainly didn't help me to absorb what he was saying or to respond to it. I was shutting my mind off inside although outwardly listening, awful that. But living in Mary and Michael's home gave me an experience of being with born-again Christians, two wonderful families, and I knew it was affecting me in certain ways. I was surprised how much they read the Bible and how well they knew it, and they weren't just reading it so that they could boast of it; they were never boastful of anything.

One matter which I was sad about was that Mary and Michael hardly ever saw any of their friends, or the wider extended family. I know we can't see everybody all the time but being involved in their church as they were seemed to mean that they no longer wished to be with others who they felt were not born-again Christians. This was all very difficult. I felt, why should people like myself and others who were doing their best to be Christians, be regarded as not so? But I had everything to learn.

We went one night to a meeting in someone's house where the music and the singing met us as we drove along the road. It was exciting. I suddenly wanted to be part of it all that particular night. Mary and Michael helped me into the wheelchair and pushed me in, and there to my surprise were two huge rooms which had a sliding door in between which had been opened out to make one very large room. Between sixty and seventy people crammed in, having a wonderful time, singing and praising the Lord. It was well-led, it was well-organised, it was sensitive and sincerely thought through, and when the pastor spoke his words were riveting. You couldn't help feel that he was talking to you personally. I'm sure everyone in the room felt the same. I will not forget that night; it's one of the many things I've always hung on to.

I stayed a week with Mary and Ted Carter in Tamworth, Northern New South Wales. It was very hot up there, but the most wonderful part of their home was in the garden, a huge swimming pool at least thirty feet long which Uncle Ted kept immaculate. Every day I spent ages in the water, which was so good for my circulation and toning up my muscles. Uncle Ted also had the local tanner stitch a sheepskin on to my wheelchair cushion, which was a joy after the heat and stickiness of the vinyl.

I spent my last week or so in Sydney with Mary and her household, now positively enjoying going with them to their church. So many things which had jarred me to begin with I found myself enjoying, but still I was most confused and full of questions. But it was wonderful to see their happiness and to know that since they'd given their lives to the Lord they had in fact become different people. That was when I began to feel close to Mary, and even though we're 12,000 miles apart, most of the time I can speak to her on the telephone and it will feel like next door and as if it was yesterday that I was with her. Soon though, it was time to leave again, but of course my excitement, as always at the thought of arriving home, was tempered by wondering how the girls and John had managed this time, and by feeling guilty again that I'd left them to manage in the harsh winter.

Another homecoming. This time, somehow, I felt out of place; everyone else was so pale at the end of February. On my return I sensed that the family had had a more difficult time while I'd been away. The girls were at a more difficult age for John to cope with and for the lady who helped them. Again the word fault comes up in large capital letters, not only about my disability affecting John and the girls, but now added to that my guilt about going away so often. This will help you understand that although Dr Lloyd had helped me enormously, I still had a way to go to feeling myself. I returned to see him on a regular basis at the Royal Infirmary as an out-patient, as before. There was so much I needed to discuss with him.

I went back to my church in Edinburgh, St Cuthbert's, under the castle where it's been since the thirteenth century. It's a beautiful church where there's always magnificent music and exceptional singing with such a good choir and choral master. I had been christened, confirmed and married there and Clare and Lisa were also christened there. I had always felt at home in this church but this time when I returned, although I still enjoyed being there and still listened intently, somehow the singing all seemed to be done by the choir; a little by the congregation but not much. I didn't feel part of it as I had in Australia. This disturbed me and confused me more. When the minister started to speak and give his address, I remember sitting waiting and counting, but there wasn't anything to count. I was waiting for him to mention the name of Jesus. Suddenly I saw my church here in Edinburgh in a totally different light. We, the congregation, were being sung to and talked to; we weren't praising the Lord, we were just sitting there on all those long pews. I felt sad. I didn't want all these feelings in my mind and felt something was missing. I kept thinking, it's just because I've been away where everything was so different. But no, it wasn't that, it was more to do with myself. St Cuthbert's hadn't changed; it had always been like that. All that Mary and Michael and Jan and Neil had shared with me, I was now looking for and couldn't find. Whereas before I had been happy I now had strong feelings of discomfort and insecurity, and felt that I wasn't a Christian after all. Yes, that came as a terrible shock. When I'd been challenged with this in Australia, frankly I thought it was just rubbish, but now, after being home for a while and trying to handle all these different thoughts and feelings and questions in my mind, I didn't seem to have anyone to share them with. I believed I'd been a Christian; in fact I had not.

The year continued and after the summer I was still not myself; it seemed to be taking ages. Clare was into an important time at the High School with her 'O' levels coming up the following summer. John, to my surprise, suggested I go again to Australia. He said, 'Why don't you take Lisa, go at the beginning of December and come back at the end of January. You'd have plenty of weeks in that time, and you could have Christmas there.'

Well, of course, Lisa was tremendously excited and Clare, bless her heart, was disappointed, but realised there was no way in which she could go at this time in her school career. So we flew to Sydney on 3rd December 1981.

The Dowlings had moved on to their own home and we saw them occasionally, which was brilliant. Again, right after our arrival, Mary said to me, 'Will you come to church with us on Sunday?' This time, instead of feeling worried about it, I was looking forward to it. It happened that Sunday that Phil Pringle, their pastor, was away speaking somewhere else and we were told that a young final year student from Bible College, Peter McHugh, would be giving the address. The service took very much the form of what I'd experienced earlier in the year: much singing, some wonderful quiet time, personal prayer time and quite a lot of reading from the Bible. After his address this young man from Bible College asked everyone to close their eyes and sit quietly and then he challenged people, anyone at all, to think about giving their life to the Lord, allowing Him to be in charge of their life, to give up their self-will. He said, if anyone felt it was the moment for them, they could either come up to the front, or if they'd rather not do that, they could stay where they were and just put their hand up quietly. I knew at that particular moment I wanted to put my hand up. I didn't have to think about it. In one moment I knew that that was what I wanted. Despite all those questions and all those many hours and months when I had felt so stressed by it all, I suddenly felt this was right. It was absolutely what I wanted to do. It didn't seem difficult, it was wonderful, it was exciting, and I felt tremendously happy. I also felt pleased that I could do it quietly in my own way, sitting where I was. There was no razzmatazz attached to it. It was extremely personal and very emotional too. There were lots of tears mixed up with happiness.

But another feeling started coming through; it was somehow a release from worry and stress. Instead of trying to work things out my way all the time, I believed then, and still do now, that because I asked the Lord to do so, He was now in charge of me. That doesn't mean, of course, that things became easier. It didn't alter for a moment the fact that I couldn't walk, had to use a wheelchair and quite likely had to expect increasing disability for the rest of my life. I hadn't sat there to ask the Lord to heal me and enable me to walk. Quite the opposite. Instead of asking for anything, I was giving up my self-will, not realising what a joy that would be until the moment came when I did it. At the end of the service Mary and Michael turned round and were so thrilled for me about what I'd just done. I was beginning to experience the happiness that they'd been feeling for some years now, which I had not understood until this moment. What did I really feel like? I think singingly happy would be one way of describing it. I felt as if I was smiling all the time, a funny way of putting it, yes, such happiness and calm inside and even though I hadn't any idea what would happen to me in the coming years, however hard it might be, I felt totally reassured that the Lord would be beside me, surrounding me, beneath me as a sure foundation, above me as an umbrella to save me from the rain of pain and fear and doubts. And He would be beside me in everything, in my thinking and in my happiness, in my sadness, totally and utterly. It was how I felt then and how indeed I still feel now, all these years later.

Even though I was so new to it all, I understood right from the beginning that I would have to play my part. I'd heard the Hardimans and the Dowlings speak about being a light for the Lord, to tell people of Jesus and to be an example. That would be a discipline. I immediately thought of how little I knew in any great depth of the Bible. I certainly couldn't quote passages from any particular book. My understanding up to then I felt had been at a very shallow level. What I'd done that morning in asking the Lord to be in charge of my life had changed my attitude, my feelings, my understanding on absolutely everything. Yes, everything. I listened with a much more open mind to what people said and how they said it. I felt as if I'd been picked up and turned round to face the world and everything in it from a different viewpoint, including all those who I loved most and everyone I was going to come in contact with. I saw them just that little bit differently from how I had before. It's helped me in the years since to be more patient, to be more understanding, less judgmental, and I've learned after quite some time that when I can manage to put the other person first and myself last, this is a wonderful way of sorting things out. It takes away misunderstanding, doubt and fear.

By now everyone was making plans for Christmas there in Sydney and Lisa and I had been invited by Aunty Helen and Peter Fitzsimons to join their large family down at their house at Newport, called Nantucket. To be at the surf was going to be a great thrill for both Lisa and me. I couldn't wait to have the opportunity of being in the water every day and I knew that with so many of my cousins who are big strong young men I would have the chance of going in the surf with their help. I also had plans to see my cousin Helen and her husband John Sides on their sheep station, but when I'd declared my feelings about this, everyone without exception in the extended family around Sydney, had said to me, 'Angela, it's just not right that you should even think of such a thing this year. Helen and John are going through a terrible time up there. They've got a serious drought and have had it for years. It's no time for them to be having visitors like you and Lisa; there are enough problems without having extra people to stay.' Of course I naturally felt, well, I wouldn't dream of imposing on them, but equally I knew that my cousin Helen and I were close enough friends as well as being cousins for me to ask her directly myself. When I rang her to see what she thought about a visit, after Christmas sometime, she said, 'Oh, we'd be delighted, it would be absolutely wonderful to have some new faces about. A diversion would be a huge help.'

'Are you absolutely sure, Helen?'

She said, 'Of course I am, you know I wouldn't say so otherwise.'

The plan was that we would go on the day before Hogmanay to their sheep station Amoila.

The week up to Christmas was an exciting time, trying to get some little presents, but also a mixture of sadness for both Lisa and myself. We became increasingly homesick and not in fact looking forward to Christmas Day in Australia at all, even though we were going to be with such a wonderful family, all of whom we were very fond of, and they were, they are, such tremendous fun. However we went up to Windhill first, the Fitzsimons' home on the ridge outside Sydney, where we had a couple of days before going down to the beach. There's always something special to remember about each time I've been there at Windhill. This time it wasn't an accident, it was in fact being landed by the young people. Yes, I remember saying later that would be the first and last time they would do that to me.

We were to drive down to Newport on Christmas Eve where we would meet the entire family. The young people who were up at the farm with Lisa and me, I think Trish and little Pete and maybe one or two of their friends, said to Lisa in the early afternoon, 'Oh, you must come with us, Lisa, and your mum can come with Mum and Dad. They come a little bit later but you could come in the advance party with us and we'll set up everything down at Newport for their arrival.'

I thought, that sounds an excellent idea. I knew Lisa would prefer to be with the young people and I didn't think any more of it. They all departed at about 3 p.m. Nobody said anything in particular; it seemed quite the normal thing for the younger people to go first. I found Aunty Helen in the kitchen. The temperature must have been at least 92°. All I had on was a sundress. Doing much made me very hot, but there was Aunty Helen in her kitchen. She had the entire contents of the freezer out on the worktops.

'Aunty Helen, whatever are you doing?' I said.

'Oh, it's my usual thing every Christmas Eve, Angela; I like to have the house spick and span to return to for the New Year.'

I suddenly realised this would mean hours and hours of work before there would be any chance of going to the coast. There was nothing for it but to get stuck in there, sideways on to the sink, with my back to the Aga, still on in that 92° heat. I washed up, and I dried up. The piles of dishes and containers seemed never ending. When we'd done the freezer we worked our way right through the kitchen until it was absolutely gleaming and then Aunty Helen said, 'How about a little sit outside on the verandah, Angela, and a cool drink?' Wonderful, I thought.

I trundled my wheelchair out to the side verandah and Aunty Helen brought three cool drinks for Peter, me and herself. We sat there quietly; it was lovely, the peace of it. The shade of the verandah couldn't prevent the glaring heat invading us but somehow the peacefulness of their garden, the wonderful eucalyptus trees, the green lawn beyond us, the lovely pine trees, and the beauty of their place cooled me and refreshed me. 'I think we'd better get back inside,' Aunty Helen said, 'there's an awful lot to do. I'm beginning to wonder if we'll ever get to Newport.' I returned into the house with Aunty Helen.

This time I discovered she was spring cleaning, one room at a time. This went on for several hours, with an occasional subside, as she put it, on the verandah which was much needed all round, and Peter would somehow appear from wherever he'd been working in the orchard, or getting the car ready for our journey, to have a cool drink with us. One of the times, he said, 'Angela, how about coming with me in the Moke down to the dam?' I couldn't resist it, 'Oh wonderful, thank you, I'd love to,' but part of me felt guilty knowing that it would mean Aunty Helen left on her own doing it all herself. Not that I could be a first class help sitting in a wheelchair, but I could be some use, and I was happy to be so.

I had on a mint green cotton sun dress, loose, comfortable and cool as the colour suggests. Uncle Pete helped me from my wheelchair into the Mini Moke, and I hung on carefully as he drove down the bumpy track to the dam. The very sight of the water cooled me down. It's amazing what an effect it can have. The silence and the peace of such a place is an experience I'll never forget but we knew that Aunty Helen was still beavering away at the house, so back we came and in I went in my wheelchair.

After what seemed such an age Aunty Helen said, 'Now I need to do my packing.' By this time it was about 10 p.m. It's a good hour and twenty minutes, going fast, from their home at Windhill, Peates Ridge, down to Newport. Somehow it became important to me to get there before midnight. I didn't want to be travelling on what was Christmas Eve into Christmas Day. My homesickness was overwhelming me again, but I didn't say much of it.

Aunty Helen's packing took only a few minutes. 'I need a cardboard box, Angela,' she said, 'can you see one about anywhere? There's usually plenty.' I quickly found one and to my amazement I watched her throw in a cossie, a towelling overdress, one or two cotton skirts and blouses, some bits of underwear and the usual things for washing. She was wearing her famous towelling hat. 'Well, that's that, I won't need any more than that, I think we're ready.' I thought, if all of us could pack like that wouldn't it be wonderful?

Aunty Helen drove fairly fast, but she's a good driver, down to Newport and there we arrived at the beach house, just coming up to midnight, with all the young people and their wives, husbands, partners, children all there and Lisa, to greet us. They had fairy lights up on the verandah and I could see the Christmas tree with its lights on, already decorated, there in the main room in the centre of the house. Suddenly my homesickness was overwhelming me again, even though I had Lisa with me and we were surrounded by such wonderful, wonderful close family.

On Christmas morning the entire household was awake early. Sitting there amongst all my cousins and Aunty Helen and Uncle Peter, with their children and young friends, Lisa and I were drowning in our homesickness. On the surface we were joining in, but underneath we longed for home, even if it was cold and dark and maybe wet. Even the thought that that wonderful frothy surf was pounding the beach of Newport there, only three hundred yards down the road, even that didn't seem to stop our misery. Phoning home was ghastly. We wanted so to do it, but afterwards were even more miserable.

I remember we went to a surf carnival on Boxing Day and that was an enormous amount of fun, and once we got past that our homesickness disappeared as we delighted in the water and the sun and only having to wear a costume and throw over something.

The household was a tremendously busy and happy one. It had one or two problems for me. It was quite a tight fit in the bathroom with my wheelchair, but I managed, and I sat on a chair in the shower. Showers are slippy, I had to watch that. But with so many big strong people around it was never a bother to have the help that I needed, which minimised the fact of needing it.

Down to the surf, those marvellous tall Fitzsimons lads took me. Nothing was too much trouble. I was so excited at the thought of going in the water, not confident of how I would manage, but completely relaxed that they were going to be with me. 'What about a go on one of the surfboards?' they said. I thought, why ever not? I'd done it lots of times all those years before, therefore I knew what to do. They were with me and indeed took me out beyond the break and got me on the board, chose the wave they thought would be best and there I was whizzing through the water towards the beach, exhilarated, excited, I was managing it. But all too quickly something awful happened. I didn't know at that minute what had happened, but suddenly I was ploughing into this wave and being tumbled round and round, and the water, full of sand, seemed to be going up my nose, coming out of my ears, was definitely in my eyes and going down my throat. It felt like drowning, although I wasn't. The water was quite shallow where all this happened, but it did give me an awful fright and it took my breath away and completely wrecked any false confidence that I might have had initially. The guys were great and came rushing forward to collect me together. Even better still, they encouraged me to have another go. 'We've thought about it, I'm sorry, we should have thought before, but if one of us were to come behind you on the board or better still one of the younger children, it would keep the nose of the board up and then you wouldn't have another time like that.'

I thought I couldn't handle another time like that. 'Okay,' I said, in the way you do when you're wanting to do something, but scared at the same time. Out we went again, beyond the break, and again they chose a wave for me, keeping a close eye that it wasn't a really big one, and also that it didn't look as if it was going to be a sand dumper. One of the younger children came on the back of the board, keeping the nose up, and it was just fine. What a thrill, simply wonderful. So we did it again and again, Aunty Helen and Uncle Peter and some of the others in the family had come onto the beach and were amazed at the fact that I was in the surf and enjoying it so much. Lisa had been standing there watching all the time. I have to admit, I was so busy enjoying myself, that I didn't look too closely at how she was at that moment.

We were only there a few days, but loved every minute of it. And then we were off up to my cousin Helen and John on their sheep station. Knowing they were in a severe drought we knew not to expect other than searing heat and no water to cool down in. So when we touched down at Griffith airport it was a shock to see a green neatly mown lawn, with a sprinkler on it, instead of bare earth. I couldn't wait to ask Helen and John how could it be, that water was being used like that when there was such a shortage. They then explained how there were channels that had been built many years ago to bring the water down so that some parts within a drought stricken area can have plenty of water, whereas others quite close are completely without. It was all very confusing, Lisa and I thought, but it was to be even more so. We drove out the usual way to their property, excitement mounting. Who was going to see the first kangaroo? As soon as we left the airport, the dirt looked bare. There wasn't a blade of grass. But when we arrived at their house there was another surprise. I knew of their swimming pool but I never expected there to be anything in it this time. But yes, there it was, sparkling blue the water, and the immediate garden just round their house was also green and the shrubs and flowers looked fine. So complicated, I couldn't understand it. They explained again how they also were fortunate to have water come down the channels and they could afford to have a pool and keep their garden irrigated just around the house. Arriving on Hogmanay, it couldn't have been more different from home. It was very hot, and there were just a few of us: Helen, John, Lisa and myself and three of their children. We weren't up late. After dinner we played some games, had a few drinks, and all stood round in a circle holding hands singing 'Auld Lang Syne'. But the next day we learned something traditional for them on the sheep station.

The New Year dawned hot and Helen was busy in the kitchen. 'Every year we do this,' she said, 'we all make up an enormous picnic, including everything we need for barbecuing, and all the families join together for a fun day out on the banks of the Murrumbidgee River. Take your cossies, it'll be hot, you'll need a swim. There'll be water skiing and different things the young people are doing, Lisa, you might like to try.'

Lisa had never done anything like that before, but she was usually game to have a try. When we arrived at the picnic place there seemed to be masses of people. They were all their friends, and families of their friends, and they all of course knew each other well, but we didn't feel outsiders in any way. Australians have an amazing gift of making you feel they've known you forever. Lisa quickly got in with the younger ones and I did know some of the older ones. The men got going with the barbecuing, that seemed to be the tradition. The women had, after all, made the food. The children were enjoying the boat on the river. It was fairly steep going down to the water, so I thought, not in my wheelchair, but we had a wonderful view of what the youngsters were doing.

And there on the water the kids were taking it in turn to water-ski up the river. I wondered if Lisa was going to have a shot. I'll never forget her rainbow coloured swimsuit. I saw her putting on the water-skis, I watched, delighted but also apprehensive as I saw her hold the rope with both hands and sit back in the water as you do. I also noticed how all the Australians, varying in age, but particularly the teenagers, were staring intently at her. You could feel it, you could sense their thinking, I bet she won't manage this, a girl out from Scotland won't have a clue. Indeed she'd never done it, but my heart was singing as that boat took off up the river with Lisa amazingly coming up out of the water straightening her legs, arms outstretched in front of her, leaning back, doing all the things she needed to do to go on up that river and round the bend out of sight. Amazement from everybody, almost disappointment on the faces of the youngsters. They couldn't believe it.

'I bet she's done it before,' they said.

'No, honestly, she hasn't. Probably just beginner's luck.'

Well that's as maybe, but it gave her much confidence with a group of young people whom she hadn't met before and it was a wonderful start to that picnic.

You could smell the barbecue, delicious. There always are a lot of flies in the country and you just get used to them. We'd had mosquitoes and they'd bitten Lisa badly down at the coast, but we hadn't been too badly bothered by the flies as so many of the homes have screens on them which helps a lot. But out there in the open with this wonderful barbecue picnic by the muddy waters of the Murrumbidgee River it was a different matter. We were all sitting expectantly waiting for the young ones, as they were kindly going to bring round the food on paper plates. Barbecued chops, sausages, delicious salads, excellent dressings, potato salad, a great favourite out there, grated carrot with orange juice on it, very colourful indeed.

Someone placed a plate on my lap, with a knife and fork wrapped in a white napkin. It smelt delicious, but as I looked down at my plate to enjoy the thought of eating it, to my horror it was absolutely covered in black flies, so much so that I couldn't see the food. My instincts were alert to the fact that eyes were upon me. I felt they were waiting for me to make a fuss and say how horrible, how ghastly and that I wouldn't eat it. But I just wafted my hands around, the flies soon moved off, I undid my napkin, took some of the tomato sauce that was being offered to me, and got on with it. Nobody said anything, but I felt inwardly pleased that I'd managed it. The Aussies love to see somebody from somewhere else not manage to cope with their environment. I wasn't going to let them have the satisfaction, sitting under the tall gum trees there, some with their white bark and others different colours, and those pale dull green eucalyptus leaves.

There was a general buzz of conversation but quieter now as most people were eating, and then we were pleased to subside after our lunch. Even the youngsters were quieter and lying about on rugs. It was lovely to watch the curling smoke of the barbecue fires, not charcoal fires, but wood fires, giving the food a different flavour from that which we knew from barbecuing back home. It was a special New Year's Day to remember.

Lisa and I just adored it on the sheep station and spent the week happily sharing all their country activities. We had no wish at all to go back to the city. The very thought of it appalled us but of course the day did dawn when we were due to pack up and fly the next day back to Sydney. For whatever reason, I don't know what it was, the airline phoned the house and said they hoped it wouldn't inconvenience us, but the flight was going to leave two hours earlier from Griffith. Two hours is not a long time, I know, but suddenly to Lisa and me, it seemed as if our wonderful time was being desperately cut short. Out of proportion, I know, but that's how we felt.

Lisa burst into tears and ran along the hall to the room which she and

Melinda had been sharing and we could hear her crying from the other end of the house. Helen was wonderful and she said, 'Leave it to me, Angela, I'll go and have a chat with her.' It seemed ages before either of them came out of the room, and when they did it was Helen who came first. She took me aside to another room and said, 'Angela, there's an awful lot more to this than we realise. Lisa has poured her little heart out to me, and this lovely holiday you've brought her on, she aged only eleven, she says to me she felt, has felt and indeed still does feel that she is meant to be responsible for you and looking after you on this trip. And as well as that she's described to me in great detail her absolute terror when you were down at Newport and the young people took you in the surf. Lisa, watching all of this, thought that you were going to drown, Angela.'

I was simply horrified to hear all this from Helen. I was so shocked and utterly miserable to think that I had caused Lisa all this distress. I had never ever thought of the fact that she might feel anything like this, responsible for me; it had never crossed my mind. How insensitive could I be, I thought, how could I be so blind to it all? Helen was marvellous in trying to help me cope with all of these feelings and to reassure me, but I felt it must have been a nightmare for Lisa instead of a happy holiday. I could understand that for her, seeing me in the water particularly that day when I came off the board and I was tumbled about, she could well have thought that I was drowning. I did swallow a lot of water and it was a scary moment for me, but because I had been used to doing things like that in Australia with my cousins, I hadn't thought of how it would seem to Lisa. I didn't feel much of a mum at that moment. I'll probably never know most of it, or the half of it. People were trying to protect me from the feelings I was at that moment having. It was definitely one of the times during all these years when I've felt my disability had caused pain to someone I loved very much.

When we arrived in Sydney Mary found Lisa and me miserable. We were tired, not just from the journey, but from so much emotion. I slept well. Of course we soon got into the city ways and there was much to enjoy with all our family and friends during the time we still had in Australia.

CHAPTER TWENTY-FIVE

Lisa was taking home a yellow polystyrene surfboard which she'd won in a beach carnival. I was taking home with me my new commitment, having asked Jesus to be in charge of me. I remember one of the Australian ministers saying that a Christian should not worry. How very difficult to achieve. We all worry to a greater or lesser extent about many things, but he'd talked it through and said if we had a true belief that the Lord will and does help us, then that should remove our worry. It was early days for me to achieve that all the time and I think it's true to say that it took quite a number of years. It does make an enormous difference. It doesn't remove all problems, but I know and experience a sure foundation of support and understanding. I never feel alone. I find myself so much happier. I know these words may sound over the top in many ways to many people who might read this. I can only tell you honestly and openly how it is for me and how I feel, and share that with you. But at the same time I also had in my mind the determination that when I arrived home, I was not going to shout it from the rooftops. I was going to wait and see if anybody asked me what I'd been doing, or if they noticed that I was different in any way. It had troubled me often that the enthusiasm of the charismatic born-again Christians often put others off. I had felt like that the year before when I had been in Australia with them all. I don't believe that just because one person has had this wonderful experience that other people should be made to feel inferior. I'm determined that whenever I can, if there is an opportunity to speak about my commitment to the Lord and what it means to me, I will be very sensitive to how others are and not jump in with both feet as it were. A trifle difficult in a wheelchair, but you know what I mean.

We arrived home to freezing weather, having almost forgotten what it was like, but it was wonderful to be home, and I was feeling much better in myself, I mean emotionally. I was sleeping better, things did not become out of proportion as they used to. I wasn't desperately needing Dr Lloyd. I had more confidence, it seemed to be returning quite quickly. However, I felt calm in my resolve not to push onto John all that I had experienced. It's not that I didn't want to share it with him, but my main fear was that if I did it in the wrong way, it would push him away from ever wanting to feel the same.

One evening over dinner John started asking me a few questions about my holiday. We started talking and I did explain a little. I talked of Jan and Neil, and the way in which I'd made a commitment, and how it had been such a shock finding out that I hadn't been a Christian because I personally hadn't made any commitment up to that point. I do remember that during the conversation we had that night John was able to, and did in fact, quote parts of the Bible which seemed to be appropriate to what we were talking about. Inside I felt quite shocked, surprised, amazed. I thought then that although John doesn't like, or appear to like, going to church he knew far more than I had known. There was I, the one who'd made this commitment and felt that I'd taken a step forward, but that evening I felt extremely humble. We can't and we mustn't judge other people on where they are in their own walk with the Lord. Please excuse me using that expression, but it's the only way in which to describe it.

In the following weeks I went back to St Cuthbert's Church and felt sad. Where was the joyful praising? I looked around me. Most of the people attending St Cuthbert's were lovely people but they were mostly elderly, hardly any young ones. There were a number of people whom I'd known from before who met together, and I did become involved in their housegroup meetings, and the group I was in kindly agreed to come quite often to our house. John didn't mind a bit. He was excellent and he encouraged me to have these people in. He didn't mind that we were singing and praising the Lord in our house. I was just sad, though I kept it to myself, that he didn't want to join in, but I hadn't expected and didn't expect him to do so. One night one of the housegroup members said, 'All of these things, Angela, will be in the Lord's time.' That helped me to be patient. Yes, that's the calmness of it, a sure warm feeling inside that God is good, and if we allow Him, He will be in control of us and the ones whom we love.

Although Australia had improved my general health I had to admit that I wasn't as strong as I'd imagined, and a month after returning I received the most horrendous shock when I heard the news that Dr Mawdsley had died suddenly one morning, aged only fifty, one of the finest people I have met in my life, the doctor that I had come to depend upon entirely, the person I felt who had been in control of me in all the medical situations which I had to face. Despite my new commitment and all it was meaning to me, I was devastated to hear of Dr Mawdsley's death.

Our GP came to visit me one day, knowing and understanding how upset I was. She said, 'Angela, I think we'll have to have you in hospital for a spell. I know someone who will look after you.'

Immediately I was rejecting the idea and I certainly couldn't believe that there was anyone at all who could take Dr Mawdsley's place. Connie looked me straight in the eye. 'But I know that there is, Angela, and also it's somebody whom you know and like and trust.'

I honestly did not believe her. Whoever could that be?

'Well, you remember Dr Cull who was Dr Mawdsley's registrar for so many years; he's now moved from London to be consultant neurologist at the Royal Infirmary. I'm going to ask him to see you, and look after you.' With the shock that I'd just had and now this wonderful surprise, I was feeling totally numb. I wanted to believe Connie, but I couldn't take it in.

I was admitted into the Royal Infirmary and in came, the following day, Dr Cull. I remembered him instantly. The surprise was wonderful. I felt myself heaving a sigh of relief. I was not going to have to build up a friendship, a relationship, a rapport, with some strange doctor. He discussed my case with a lot of the students. I knew that it interested many because of the change of diagnosis from MS to sarcoidosis. I didn't mind, and still don't mind, being spoken about and have students or other doctors come to examine me. I have been given tremendous medical attention over many, many years; the very least I can do is to be of some use in the training of young doctors, or to increase the knowledge of others who come from different countries.

When Dr Cull returned from his round alone, and sat down for a moment, he discussed with me how I felt personally, and the various recent problems that I was having with my legs. He decided they would do nerve conduction tests which I positively hated, those needles being stuck into you. I always found it so sore. He said, 'I think we'll also give you some physiotherapy and you must rest, Angela.' Always that word, rest. I was having to get used to it. Because I felt immediately relaxed in talking to him I found myself asking him a bit more about sarcoidosis. It's true Dr Mawdsley had explained a bit, particularly when it was in my chest, but I suppose I'd never asked him directly, how did it actually affect my system? So I straight out asked Dr Cull this question. It was impulsive, I know.

He didn't say, 'Are you sure you want to know the answer?' He said, 'The sarcoid is causing deposits to be laid down in your meninges, which affects your nervous system.'

Silence, I felt, quiet. I don't know what I'd expected, but deposits laid down in the meninges of my brain seemed far more worrying than MS, and immediately I wished I hadn't asked him. I think he realised that. But on the other hand I thanked him for being open and honest about it, and of course whether I knew or not was not going to make it go away.

CHAPTER TWENTY-SIX

Over the years I've come to realise the value of physio and I love doing it. Having to make the effort myself made me feel there was a little something I could do. I realised that proper movements done on a regular basis are of enormous value to anyone like myself with a chronic disability. Without the opportunity my arms and my legs would have been much worse much more quickly. I had always been given excellent physiotherapy in whichever hospital I had been in over the many years. But that particular time I began to think of all I was having in the way of exercise in the hospital which then stopped when I went home. It seemed a waste of all the effort that was being made on my behalf in the hospital. I mentioned this to Dr Cull. 'Well,' he said, 'I don't see why you shouldn't have some domiciliary physiotherapy, it would be an excellent idea.' When I went home it was set up by Dr Gibbs that I should have this but I was informed from the start that although the physiotherapist could come a couple of times a week to begin with, it was not something they would be able to do on a regular basis. If I'd broken my leg or had some accident like that, I would have had regular physio for as long as I needed it, but because I was a chronic problem the physiotherapist could not give me ongoing support. It is a challenging thought that people like myself who have to sit in a wheelchair or with even greater difficulties, have nearly always to face the fact of becoming more sore, more stiff and more disabled as each month and year goes past. Not a good thing to be thinking about.

'Can be fun and won't be boring!' This statement was the last sentence in my first advertisement to achieve private help at home. I wanted a little notice, something different from the usual requests for help. I wanted, if possible, to have somebody local. So I wrote out a number of little white cards, saying, 'Disabled Lady Needs Help, 5 days a week, Can be Fun and Won't be Boring' and had them placed in the local post offices and newsagents. That's how I found Julia and it was the start of a wonderful time with a young lady who came to help me knowing nothing about nursing care, and not a tremendous lot about preparation of food or indeed many things that I needed help with. She was, however eager to learn, adaptable, willing, very able and full of fun, and she lived just down the road – perfect. The physiotherapist showed Julia one or two passive movements that she could do with my legs after my afternoon rest, which gave me continued help with muscle tone and circulation.

Why was I having so much help? The reason is a hard one. I felt my hands and arms were weaker and I noticed that pushing myself round in the wheelchair was not quite so easy as it had been before. I now had what they call a gloved feeling, when your hands are slightly numb. It is rather a weird uncomfortable sensation. And the other thing I was experiencing about my hands was that hot things seemed extra hot and cold things extra cold. This hypersensitivity of my feet and my hands is what the doctors call peripheral neuropathy. The harsh reality is that it's one thing to get used to sitting in a wheelchair, but I would say it's far more difficult to handle emotionally all the feelings when you have problems cutting your food, when your writing becomes much more difficult and fine movements like picking up small things are almost impossible. Certain glasses seemed more difficult than others. The ones with rough sides were easier to hold. A smooth tall glass with an iced drink in it was a nightmare: the condensation on the outside of the glass made it wet, and it would slide right through my hands. I quickly learned the nightmare of being offered a cup of coffee which I couldn't hold without spilling. Everything seemed to need to be in a mug with a handle, or in a glass with a handle.

I shall never forget my first horrendous experience of having my food cut up. We were at the house of great friends of ours; their dining room is magnificent. There were at least twenty of us. Our hostess kindly suggested that I sit at the end of the table as it would be easier for my wheelchair; she'd thought it all through carefully. There was a gentleman on either side of me, neither of whom I knew, not that that bothered me, I found it easy to talk to people. The first course, soup, was fine. I didn't have any problem with that, but I was worried about all those crystal glasses in front of me. It wasn't that I couldn't pick things up or move them around in those days but I was acutely aware that a sudden wrong movement would tip a glass over.

The main problem came when the next course arrived. It was served from a carving table behind me and smelled delicious. Roast beef and all the trimmings, wonderful vegetables and gravy, everything perfect. The plate was placed in front of me, and I looked down. For one split second I thought, how delicious, but the next second my heart sank. I knew I would not manage to cut up the meat and even some of the vegetables like roast potatoes would be difficult. All I could imagine was me splattering the food from my plate on to the table or on to my clothes. I felt totally inhibited about asking either of the gentlemen to help me. I know it seems ridiculous, but I thought it would embarrass them if I asked them to cut up my food. So I called our hostess aside and said would she do it for me at the carving table. There was no problem about it, she was very diplomatic and quietly took my plate away and brought it back. I looked down again. The food that I had seen and desired and looked forward to now looked totally different. Not appetising. I couldn't believe it. Suddenly I thought of children and realised that must be why they often push food away and say they don't want it. Of course I ate it but it was a harsh lesson and I felt sad to think that I was going to have to cope with that every day of my life.

I know it's all emotion that I'm talking about but it's overwhelming, and if you know anyone who requires such help as this and you're the person giving it, I urge you to think of what I've just shared with you. I managed dinner that night, not knowing that there was another challenge to come. We went through to the drawing-room for coffee, which was brought in on a trolley. Those beautiful delicate small coffee cups are delightful to drink out of but not for someone like myself, because as the cup was placed on the small table at the side of my wheelchair, I realised that not only would I be clumsy at picking it up, but also that the little tiny handle would probably trap my finger and I would not be able to put it down again. I asked if I could have my coffee in a mug, realising now that there's no good trying to pretend about any of these things. It wouldn't help me and it wouldn't help those around me and the only thing to do is to make the very least of it and not show the emotion. It's too much for others, but I did share it with John and the girls and our close friends; they're wonderful always in helping me with such matters.

Later on, when I found my right hand, which had always been my strongest, to be much weaker than my left, I learned to eat with my left hand all the time. I couldn't help laughing in my unhappiness at how all those years I'd trained the girls to have polite table manners, to keep their elbows in, and things like that. Now suddenly I had to use my left hand and I couldn't balance my food without my elbow being out. It was much wiser to swallow my pride and have a white napkin tucked up, 'like the French do,' as someone kindly said. I continued to have huge inhibitions about my food being cut up until one day a long-standing friend of the family, Ronald Parker, was visiting and he was asking how I was generally, and I mentioned to him this emotion I was having about eating with a fork all the time. 'But, Angela,' he said, 'think of it, the entire population of the United States of America do just that, everybody does it.' I remember smiling and giving him a big hug. In a moment he dispelled all my stress and embarrassment.

And how was I managing with everything else? A nurse now came to help me have a bath. I needed some help with dressing. I was still managing the loo all right but, as I mentioned earlier, pushing myself about in the wheelchair was tiring me very quickly. I received a power wheelchair from the NHS which was of enormous help getting around the house, so that wasn't tiring me, but this particular chair was not supposed to go outside, not even into the garden, certainly not along the pavement.

My problem was that to change wheelchairs entailed so much difficulty, not only for myself but for anybody with me, that increasingly I did go out in my power chair which was only supposed to be for inside. I felt guilty about that, but at the same time it gave me a wonderful freedom to be able to move at some speed both round our paved part of the garden and along the pavement down to the shops. They would have given me a different chair, a much bigger one and more clumsy with larger wheels which would have been allowed outside, but I felt it was so huge to have round the house.

I was back with emotions which I wasn't handling. Feeling clumsy in the big wheelchair – ugly, yes, I think that's the word which comes to mind. So for that reason I persisted with the indoor power chair and had to admit that, increasingly, I needed somebody to push me around when in my ordinary chair. It's not the same. When somebody else has to push you around somehow you're always facing the wrong way. If somebody comes to speak to you and they're behind you, you can't turn round naturally unless the person with you judges it absolutely right. However well they know you, it's extremely difficult. Going round an art gallery, how often do we wish to go forward and then step back to view a painting in a different light or from a different distance? How impossible it is to read those little cards beside each work of art. You have to go forward and then step back. I couldn't do that myself any more and it was a lot of work for anybody with me. Many, many problems which I hadn't coped with before were now presenting themselves to me and those who helped me.

Julia was fantastic. Although she was so slim, she seemed so strong. I know that sometimes when we were out, she had this way of, how can I say, transferring me sideways from my car to my wheelchair, all in a moment she did it. Many times a man would step forward to see if he could help and always she would say, 'No thank you, I can manage fine,' and to his total amazement she would do just that, despite her apparent slender frame. These things worried me, but then I learned that I could have a special seat in my car which could turn around and come out over the side of the car and allow me to transfer myself from the car seat into my wheelchair. That was an enormous help.

CHAPTER TWENTY-SEVEN

On 24 February 1984 I received a most interesting letter from someone I had never met, Geoffrey Lord, who was then the secretary of the Carnegie United Kingdom Trust, based in Dunfermline. In the letter he outlined a plan that he had, you could say a vision, for disabled people to enjoy the arts, whether they were at home, in the community, in hospital or needed help to get to different arts venues. He invited me to attend a meeting to be held at the Disability Scotland office where he hoped to gather together a number of people who might be interested in this project. I had of course heard of the Carnegie Trust, but didn't know very much about what they achieved. But as I read the invitation I remembered a recent meeting when I had met two charming ladies, Theresa Wallace and Valerie Nimmo, at a City of Edinburgh Access panel meeting. They had come to share with the panel what they were doing for the Richard Attenborough report on Arts for Disabled People. They had been given a remit for a year to find out what needs disabled people had and how well or not the different arts venues catered for these needs, and also to take account of the attitude of people who ran arts organisations, whether theatres, cinemas, concert halls or whatever. A most interesting remit I thought. It had all sounded exciting, interesting and an excellent thing to do, but I have to confess that as I sat there, not the only disabled person round the table I might add, my mind became troubled, because I was thinking, how would they know what it feels like to have a disability? Would they really know the dimensions of a wheelchair or the needs of a person who is deaf or blind? I knew myself that I couldn't answer all those questions either, so I asked them about these aspects of what they were doing. They were both concerned and embarrassed but they were excellent in replying, that my question made them realise that maybe they should have, if possible, a person with a disability with them at each visit who could speak face to face with different venue managers. Subsequently they asked me if I would join them on some of their visits. They often spoke of Geoffrey Lord and that was when I first heard of him.

When I attended the meeting there were, I thought, a large number of people at it, probably between twenty and thirty, and such an interesting mix.

A couple of us in wheelchairs, somebody who was extremely deaf, a person who was blind, a dancer, several artists who had already worked with disabled people, lawyers, an architect, an accountant, and a range of people who would have the ability to run a company which Mr Lord told us he wished to call Artlink. Artlink would receive initial funding from The Carnegie United Kingdom Trust, with the clear understanding that it would immediately work for and achieve other funding from different sources: District Councils, hospitals, communities and hopefully the Scottish Arts Council, businesses and trusts. Such funding would require enormous effort, skill and initiative to achieve. Artlink's aims would be to enable disabled and elderly people to enjoy art activity, whether they were in hospitals, at home, or in the community. Through the work of the administrator and guidance of the Artlink Council, artists would be funded to use their skills with the disabled and elderly people, who would choose themselves whatever they wished to do. For the first time in the United Kingdom, an escort service staffed by volunteers would enable people to choose some art activity and have a person to share it with, assistance with transport and access to venues.

I was most interested. It was fascinating. I felt I could contribute something, I liked the people, and the mixture, excellent. Here was integration, right round that table, with one aim. In the next few months there were several meetings with people who were interested and who Mr Lord felt could contribute, and a company was set up. Even although I didn't have the knowledge of how to set up a company, like others around the table I could contribute on both the physical and emotional needs of people, the sensitive side which sometimes is difficult for others to know of when they haven't experienced it.

When the summer came, it was all accomplished, and Artlink was registered as a charitable company. Up until then Geoffrey Lord had chaired the majority of the meetings, but it was decided that they would need to appoint a chairman and vice chairman, and maybe for a few meetings people might take it in turns to take the chair, which indeed is what they did.

Then came a phone call one evening, a lovely warm summer evening which I'll always remember. It was Alan Turner, another council member of Artlink. He said, 'Angela, we've all been thinking and decided that we'd like you to take the chair of Artlink.'

I was absolutely horrified. 'I couldn't possibly, Alan,' I said, 'I just couldn't do it, I know I couldn't. Why on earth ask me when you have all those excellent people with business acumen round the table who could chair the meetings properly, not someone like myself who would be a total amateur.'

'No,' he said, 'Angela, we've decided that it would be best if you did it.'

I said, 'But Alan, with the best will in the world I couldn't do it, I can't. I'm always happy to do my best and I want to continue contributing to Artlink, I think it's an excellent organisation and it's going to have hopefully a wonderful future, but please don't ask me to do this, because I don't have the skills required.' I was adamant in my feelings.

Alan persisted. 'Well,' he said, 'I tell you what, I'll let you sleep on it.'

'But it won't make any difference, Alan, I know, I'm absolutely definite about this. Thank you, but no thank you.'

Again he said, 'Well, I'll ring you in the morning, Angela.'

I didn't know what else to say, but goodbye.

I went out into the garden and then John arrived home. I couldn't wait to tell him about the phone call. 'How about I pour some sherry?' John said. I thought, yes, I could certainly do with something. There wasn't any part of me that felt it would be a good idea to accept what Alan Turner had asked me to do, and that's what I told John. But he said to me, as we sipped our drinks, 'Angela, why are you turning down something which you don't really know anything about?'

I said, 'But that is the point, John, I don't know anything about chairing meetings and the business side of things.'

'Well, I'm sure they have their reasons,' John said. 'Won't you even consider it?'

No, I couldn't, I said. I still insisted there was no way I could do that. John can be very persuasive and firmly so. He continued by saying, 'It seems a great pity that you're saying "no" like that before even finding out whether you could manage and how it would be.'

I could feel my mind working overtime. My attitude was shifting slightly. Indeed by the time that evening was over, I had promised John that I would at least try it, but as we'd been talking out there in the garden another strong feeling came over me and it was this: if I were to take on what seemed an enormous job, I would have to give it a hundred per cent; I didn't see how I could do it just for the odd meeting. I hope you understand that. I knew it would mean a huge learning process for myself, but hopefully, hopefully I might manage it, but it would need to be better than just managing it. If I were to do it, I would want to do it not just well, but very well. So many thoughts running through my mind.

The following morning Alan Turner phoned again. 'Well,' he said, 'what do you think, Angela, I do hope you've changed your mind.'

'Well, Alan, I haven't changed it really, but John's changed it for me.'

'Oh good,' he said, 'the others will be delighted, we'll all be delighted if you would do this, Angela. Thank you very much. I'll be in touch. Geoffrey and

I will come round and we can have a meeting and discuss various things with you at your house before your first council meeting.'

When I came off the phone, I thought, whatever have I agreed to? All sorts of things came flying through my mind, mostly problems of how on earth I would do the right thing in front of all those business people. Since we were just a newly formed registered charity Artlink had no premises of its own, so we were most fortunate to be able to continue to have our meetings at Disability Scotland.

After considerable help from Geoffrey and Alan the day came when I was to chair my first Council Meeting. I drove myself and parked my car on a little street alongside the Caledonian Hotel. I got out into my wheelchair, with my usual problems. Being an evening meeting I knew the traffic would be a nightmare, so I'd given myself lots of time. I made my way with difficulty across the road and into the building which fortunately was accessible. I got someone to press the button for the lift. I was nervous to a degree which I'd never experienced before; I just couldn't imagine how I was going to manage in this totally new situation. I felt people would be expecting such a lot of me. The butterflies in my tummy were flipping, I would say.

The conference room was a fairly long one and we'd been holding the meetings there, but somehow the table seemed even longer when I found myself placed at one end of it with all these people arranged at either side and at the other end as well. I suppose it was in my nervousness that I said, 'Good evening, ladies and gentlemen, I'm afraid the meeting will have to be Angela Dobbie's way, since as you know I do not have the experience of business meetings and how you would normally run them.'

Everybody laughed. It broke the ice and helped me. And then to my surprise, somebody raised their hand and said, was I going to be called Madam Chairman or Chairman or Chairperson? Well, I was completely taken aback; I had never thought of any such thing. Various people had some strong ideas on the matter. The women generally seemed keen that I would be called the Chairperson or Madam Chairman. There seemed to be a lot of conflict around the table. Sitting where I was, I thought, this is ridiculous. We're all spending time on discussing something so petty and I felt myself that we should keep it as Chairman which had been the usual way. I couldn't see any need for having anything different. We took a vote on it; it was absolutely even.

Then someone piped up, 'Well, Madam Chairman, you have a casting vote, what do you say?'

Instantly I said, 'I think it should be Chairman, not Chairperson or any of these other ideas; that is what I would wish.' Everybody seemed to be more than happy with that. I think all that little discussion rather helped me to gain confidence and indeed the meeting which I thought would be more than a nightmare, wasn't at all. We had an agenda, and I had had my discussions with Geoffrey and Alan and others, and I knew what was coming up and it seemed nowhere near as difficult as I had thought.

CHAPTER TWENTY-EIGHT

Had it not been for John's persistent persuasion, I would have turned down this wonderful opportunity to go through a new door in my life, called Artlink. As each day went by, and the board of Artlink looked around to rent premises in Edinburgh and to advertise for an administrator, I became increasingly conscious of the fact that, although I had much to learn on the business side, I was helped by experience through the different strands of my life. For example, the strong influence of my grandfather and my mother and being brought up in a home where we were encouraged to be outgoing, hospitable and not just kind, but sensitive, to other people. Also my nursing and midwifery training, my experience with patients in hospital and all the

John . . . the person with the most patience, understanding and self-control . . .

problems that it meant to them and their families. Then, on the other side, when I had to face the likelihood of ongoing and increasing disability there was the enormous strength that John gave me, as well as the constant boosting of my confidence and the happiness we have with each other and our children. My counselling experiences and, of course, my Access work both for the City of Edinburgh and Scotland. All these strands in my life seemed to come together for a purpose, to enable me to achieve the work involved as Chairman of Artlink.

I knew it was going to be a very daunting day when Artlink would be launched publicly at the Queen's Hall in Edinburgh. A lot of thought had gone into who should be invited. Between eighty and ninety people came, many of whom were the heads of charitable trusts, family trusts, people who would be likely to support Artlink in some way. There were also people from businesses, and a wide range of senior people in the community who could either influence the support of Artlink or themselves initiate some form of funding. We were conscious too that it was important that people such as hospital administrators, the district council and disabled people themselves should all come together to hear what we proposed to do. I, of course, gave a lot of thought as to what I would say. Geoffrey Lord and the Artlink Council were highly supportive and encouraging. It had been decided that the press would be invited, though we couldn't be sure they would come, of course. Geoffrey Lord was going to open the proceedings at the Queen's Hall, followed by Carolyn James, a very attractive lady who is an artist despite being blind, and then at twelve o'clock midday I would have to do my part.

I wrote down all sorts of ideas, scrapped most of them, spent a lot of time just thinking about it, and eventually I had a fairly clear idea in my mind of what I should say that day. Getting dressed in the morning with the help of Julia felt and was a nightmare. I was edgy, nothing seemed right. How important, as always, it was, to feel my clothes would look right, not just right, but smart, and not just smart but suitable for being in the wheelchair, especially on such a day. It was all to do with confidence, of course, and I didn't have any, not a shred. Somehow I couldn't imagine how I would do it. On the way to the Queen's Hall that day, thank goodness I did what I did. I thought and said, 'Please, Lord, be in control of me today.' I should have been saying that all the time. I had promised to believe that, all those months before, but we can slip out of doing that to our great loss.

I was still nervous, but arrived at the Queen's Hall as people were assembling there. Geoffrey and Valerie and Theresa had everything arranged. There seemed such a lot of people and to my horror I saw that they were going to dim the main lights but the lights over the desk by the platform were going

With Ronnie Corbett at the launch of the Artlink video

to be on. Unfortunately, just before it all started I caught sight of John. Whatever was he doing here? It seemed to make it worse, my nervousness doubled immediately. I know he didn't wish me to see him, but I did. I knew that he was there and that made me want to do twice as well, and how on earth would that be possible? Geoffrey opened the proceedings as planned, giving an excellent explanation about Artlink Edinburgh and the Lothians. He then introduced Carolyn James who gave an amazing talk about how she painted. We have no idea of people's potential, what they can manage. Most people, including myself, would have thought it to be quite impossible. I was listening to what she said, but my mind was going off at a tangent. I had this strong feeling that I shouldn't say most of the things that I planned, that I should take this opportunity to tell the people gathered together what it was really like to have a disability. The hours and hours of time, boring time that people have with nothing or little to do to help it pass, the loneliness, the frustration, that even if they wish to have some art activity, it would most likely be impossible through lack of access, transport and often someone to go with them.

All this was going through my mind and somehow when it was my turn to wheel my chair forward and turn around and face all the people, my nervousness seemed to vanish. I could hear myself saying the words. They were a mixture of strong gut feelings and emotions, which came pouring out of me. I sensed everyone was listening, I definitely had their attention. I have a phrase which I often use – Never Miss an Opportunity; this was one of those. I felt fired up inside, determined to make sure that all those there would know of the Nit Grit of Disability. I hoped that such an insight, spoken from my heart, would encourage the wide range of people there to support the work of Artlink.

I was privileged to be Chairman of Artlink for six years and it gave me a positive way in which to use all the experiences that I have had, Both Sides of the Fence.